What Others Say About
Choosing Energy Therapy
and Wanda Buckner

This book offers a practical guide for choosing energy healing for yourself, your children and animal companions. Wanda's life journey and experiences allow her to share her wisdom and knowledge in a manner that is easy to read and understand. Powerful anecdotal stories reveal the effectiveness of energy medicine in physical, emotional, mental and spiritual healing. All healing is a personal journey as *Choosing Energy Therapy* certainly demonstrates.

— **Lisa Mentgen-Gordon, CEO, Healing Touch Program**

Energy medicine is quickly becoming an efficient and sought after treatment in holistic and conventional settings. Wanda Buckner's love, devotion, and talent of noninvasive healing, make her the perfect guide.

— **Marie Manuchehri RN,**
author of *Intuitive Self-Healing*

This book is a resource for anyone who wonders about energy therapies. Wanda's breadth of experience, passion for the subject, and love of her practice allow her to teach us gently and clearly. Sit down with this book and a cup of tea and very soon you may be inspired to learn and practice energy healing techniques or ready to find a practitioner. Regardless, you will feel optimistic, hopeful and have a more holistic outlook regarding the path to health and balance.

— **Trisha Dawn Roisum, DVM**

Choosing Energy Therapy is an outstanding summary of energy healing techniques and their potential for improving both the human and companion animal condition. Wanda Buckner is a powerful healer whose passion for sharing her expertise will benefit many people exploring viable, effective, complementary medicine options. This book is well worth your time and attention.

— **Deborah Erickson, PhD**

Voicing the language of energy medicine requires deep familiarity with its science and philosophy combined with hands-on experience. Wanda is a strong voice for understanding the many pathways to energetic health.

— **Barbara Dahl, RN,**
Healing Touch Instructor, Emeritus

Energy therapy is a powerful, proven method to heal the body, mind and spirit. *Choosing Energy Therapy* shows you how to effectively enhance the natural healing abilities in anyone including your animal companions.

— **Robbie Holz, speaker, holistic expert and author of**
award-winning book *Secrets of Aboriginal Healing*

Wanda invites the reader to truly embrace the journey of healing, knowing that the journey is the healing, letting go of the outcome and allowing the miracles to show up.

— **Meg Haggerty, Reiki Master,**
Healing Touch Certified Practitioner

Wanda Buckner gives us a window into the world of energy medicine. What it is, what it does and how to choose a practitioner. If you or your animals are not fully healing, read this book.

— **Brett Dupree, author of** *Joyous Expansion:*
Unleashing Your Passions to Lead an Inspired Life

Do you wish you could explain energy work to others without their eyes glazing over? Do you wish someone would explain what energy work is, without all those new-age words? Wanda hits the mark here. Her writing is neutral, friendly and expertly explains in easily relatable terms what you want to know. I enjoyed how her analytical mind organized the material into a trail of breadcrumbs to follow.

— **Sarah Thorpe, Clairvoyant Reader, Healer, Intuitive**
Mind Program Instructor, Ordained Minister

Choosing Energy Therapy is an easy read for the layperson looking for basic knowledge. Wanda explains the different integrative energy modalities that complement traditional Western medicine. I recommend this book to any patients exploring integrative therapy to facilitate their healing.

— **Meg Voelker, RN, MN, RN-BC, Nurse Case Manager**

Wanda is a powerful and intuitive healer, who generously shares her wisdom with integrity, humor, and grace. This book is a gift of love. If you are holding this book, read on. Be open to the mystery and the opportunities of exploring Energy Medicine for yourself and those you love.

— **Sandra Pedersen, Healing Touch**
Certified Practitioner

Wanda has written an insightful book about the possibilities of energy therapy for making a difference in your life. Buy it. You won't regret it.

— **Andy Fracica, MBA, author of**
Navigating the Marketing Maze

Wanda Buckner brings her grounded wisdom as a doctoral-level educator and energy worker to this book. She is a lifelong student who loves to share what she learns.

— **Joanna Cummings, author of**
Kick Butts, Take Names: It's All About Freedom

Animals need holistic health options too. This book helps you decide if energy therapy could benefit those you love.

— **Keith Lawhorn, Writer, Speaker,**
Small Business Owner and Developer

A terrific book with multiple examples of how energy work complements and enhances traditional medical care.

— **June Kerr, author of** ***Rabboni, My Love:***
A Memoir of Jesus' Wife, Mary Magdalene

Filled with true stories of real-life successes, this book shows how energy therapy can make a difference in all areas of your life.

— **Janette Turner, author of** ***Penning Your Memoir***

Wanda answers your questions about energy therapy and the impact it can have on your life and the lives of those you love.

— **Terry Gargus, MS, author of** ***Reinventing Any Life***

This handbook tells you why and how to include energy work as part of your healing journey.

— **Robin O'Grady, author of** ***The Optimist's Edge:***
Moving Beyond Negativity to Create Your Amazing Life

Choosing
ENERGY
THERAPY

A Practical Guide to Healing Options
for People and Animals

AVIVA
PUBLISHING
NEW YORK

WANDA BUCKNER, EdD

Choosing Energy Therapy:
A Practical Guide to Healing Options for People and Animals
Copyright © 2014 Wanda Buckner

Address all inquiries to www.WandaBuckner.com

Published by
Aviva Publishing
Lake Placid, NY
518.523.1320
www.avivapubs.com

ISBN: 9781940984100
Library of Congress Control Number: 2014930454

Editor: Jeannine Mallory
Cover and Logo: Deborah Gotto, http://dgdesigns.businesscatalyst.com
Interior Design: Fusion Creative Works, www.fusioncw.com
Cover Photo: Sandra Lynn Fine Portraiture

Printed in the United States of America
First Edition

For additional copies, please visit www.WandaBuckner.com

Disclaimer: This book describes the use of complementary healing methods (also known as "modalities"). These modalities do not replace consultation, diagnosis and treatment by human or animal health professionals, including mental and behavioral professionals. The author and publisher are not liable or responsible for any outcomes arising from any information in this book.

Dedication

I dedicate this work to my clients, friends and family, both human and animal, who have been and continue to be my teachers. Your openness, honesty, and continuing support allow me to grow as a person and a practitioner in this journey we call healing. Your grace and presence are evident in the pages of this book and in my life.

Acknowledgments

In gratitude.

Thank you to the woman called Jane in this book whose medical crisis and death awakened within me the dormant power we all possess to bring comfort and peace to others through the influence of touch and near touch. Thank you to the individuals, nurses, doctors, and veterinarians who have written about the healing power of touch, love, and intention. Thank you to those who research, teach, and continue to explore the energetics of humans and animals.

Thank you to Bernie Clarke, RN, HTCP/I, my first energy work instructor in the heart-centered work of Healing Touch for people. When I took Healing Touch Level 1, I had no previous experience with energy healing, no knowledge of chakras, and no confidence in complementary treatments. At that time, my business was Proposal Writing and Development. I worked as an independent grant writer helping education and government agencies obtain funding to implement research based best practices verified by rigorous evaluation.

In the Healing Touch Program™ classes, I was the student with her hand up, asking if there was research to support the "allegations" made about chakras, energy and health, Healing Touch, and on and on. Bernie patiently answered all my questions about research in support of intentional touch helping the body to self-heal. Bernie never asked me to take anything on faith, to hold my questions until she finished, or to see her after class. The pace of her delivery and demonstrations allowed me time to mentally process, observe, and then practice being the giver and experience being the receiver of each technique.

Thank you to Elly Le Duc, RN, HTCP, and Sherri Cote, HTCP/I, who helped me and others solidify our skills during monthly Healing Touch practice sessions at their homes. These sessions helped me heal from the unexpected death of my partner, Lloyd Roberts in 2004. I discovered a world of healing I had never known and experienced the power of energy work to improve lives. In their last days, Elly and Lloyd showed me how people could die with dignity, humor, and no regrets, even when death seemed premature.

As my Healing Touch Program mentor, Sherri met with me monthly for a year as I struggled to understand the experiences I had as a Healing Touch Program Apprentice. Sherri was gracious, accepting, and thoughtful in her responses to my quandaries. I shared my misgivings about doing healing work, dilemmas and successes with my clients, and the extraordinary happenings during the sessions.

I began to hear and see people who had died as well as people who were still alive. I listened to their conversations and saw replays of moments in the clients' lives. Sometimes I saw angels! I told Sherri, "Things are happening in that room that

I don't believe in!" She didn't deny any of these phenomena. She just said, "Now you do."

Thank you to Carol Komitor, Founder of Healing Touch for Animals®. She taught me, and hundreds more, about the differences between the auras of animals and humans, that lead to the differences in the treatment protocols. Her vision inspired and informed my work.

Thank you to Kim Martin, DVM and acupuncturist, and Trish Roisum, DVM, acupuncturist, and chiropractor, who allowed me to learn from them and team with them for the greatest good of their patients. We witnessed the power of using multiple interventions—conventional and holistic veterinary care, acupuncture, chiropractic, aromatherapy and Healing Touch— to support the healing and continuing health of animals.

Thank you to Joanna Cummings for her continuing friendship from my early client sessions through the writing of this book. Her example of putting herself fearlessly on the line as Nicci Tina, dressed as a giant cigarette butt, is a continuing inspiration.

Thank you to Patrick Snow, my writing/speaking coach. He kept my focus on the product: getting it done was more important than doing it perfectly. Without his push, I might still be polishing this manuscript.

Thank you to my partner, John Hawthorne, who continues to encourage and support my dreams, and love me unconditionally.

Thank you to my son, Stephen Brace, who has witnessed my many transformations. When I began reading auras, he told me, "Mom, you've come full circle! You're back to the 60's."

Thank you to my clients who provided invaluable feedback that helped me transition from proposal development and writing to my current business, Healing Energy Services. I appreciate the willingness of clients to share their personal stories so others may learn. I also thank the human and animal clients who continue to be my teachers and support as I explore the possibilities of healing through energy therapy.

Contents

Foreword

In our busy everyday lives, it often seems difficult to make just one more decision. When it comes to our healthcare, figuring out what needs to be done and whom to go to is often daunting. The fact that we have to tell yet another healthcare provider our medical or emotional history or the events from years past sometimes brings us to a point of not exploring all the possibilities for our well-being.

Choosing Energy Therapy: A Practical Guide to Health Options for People and Animals presents opportunities and does not make claims that one energy therapy is better than another. Wanda gives individuals a directional invitation to help them make clear decisions and find the best approach to energy therapy. She demonstrates that qualified and caring people offer a variety of choices to support our health through energy medicine, and that a healthy energy system supports the body's health.

This book lends itself to the ease of blending medical research with different healing practices. Wanda shares personal accounts of recipients who receive healing and individual practitioners who share their expertise. In these pages, you will find stories that validate the particular issues at hand, and the accountability of different ways to assist one in their own healing, be it humans or animals. The stories tell the great successes of energy healing modalities, as well as the heartbreaking challenges that sometimes show up as life unfolds. Wanda brings each of her stories to our hearts and sets up a way to empower us so that we make the best decisions for ourselves and our animals.

Wanda models the cooperative presence of traditional and holistic approaches to healing without ownership. She includes other healthcare providers as possible solutions to a healing crisis or for accelerating greater spiritual connections. Many references are offered to validate and direct the reader's search for the truth.

This writing brings no claim to fame, nor sought-after accolades. The information shared throughout *Choosing Energy Therapy* is filled with heart and the foundational pieces to help make clear healing choices. Wanda brings her best in all she does, and this book is no exception.

— Carol Komitor, Founder of Healing Touch for Animals®

Introduction

DISCOVERING ENERGY THERAPY

You may have doubts about healing modalities that purport to clear, balance and support the body's energetic system so the person or animal can self-heal physically, emotionally, mentally and spiritually. In the following pages, you will find answers to your questions and guidance about energy therapy and practitioners. We cannot deny the energetic basis of our cells and body processes. The medical community knows that specific levels of electrical current support tissue and bone to heal. Doesn't this imply that energy flowing from our hands can also positively affect healing?

You may be dissatisfied with the current health care treatments and program you have relied on for yourself, your family, and your animals. You probably already pay attention to prevention and seek medical treatment as needed. However, these measures may not be enough for you to experience vibrant health and well-being. The stress and demands of daily life weigh heavily some days and weeks. You aren't sick enough to see a doctor or depressed enough to see a counselor, but do not enjoy life to the fullest.

Are you looking for a natural, non-invasive, non-chemical way to support your health and the health of those you love? Are you tired of just feeling okay? Do you want vibrant spiritual, emotional, mental, and physical well-being for yourself and your animals?

We have a plethora of health care options and alternatives to select from, including complementary treatments that work with the energetic fields within and around the body. These interventions go by various names—Healing Touch, Therapeutic Touch, Reiki, Reconnective Healing, Matrix Energetics—with more being added every year.

Let me be your guide to choosing therapies that work with the energetic system to clear and balance it and promote improved well-being in all areas of your life—physical, emotional, mental, and spiritual. As George D. Lundberg, MD, former Editor-in-Chief, Journal of the American Medical Association, maintains, "There is no complementary or alternative medicine. There is only medicine; medicine that has been tested and found to be safe and effective—use it; pay for it. Medicine that has been tested and found not to be safe and effective—don't use it; don't pay for it."

Energy therapy comes in many forms, but it is always noninvasive, risk free, relaxing, and comparatively low cost. A session with an energy practitioner will not leave you drugged, sluggish, or confused as some medications do. You may have an amazing emotional or spiritual experience, you may get off the treatment table pain free, or you may experience nothing during the session. While it is satisfying to see colors, images and visions on the treatment table, these experiences are irrelevant to the value of the session. Your healing may be instantaneous or it may unfold in the days that follow.

Perhaps you live with animals that are anxious, fearful, painful, or unhappy. Western and Eastern medicine help, but may not be enough to bring the animals into the fullness of who they can be. Energy therapy makes a difference. We don't know how animals experience energy work internally, but we can observe their bodies' soften as deep relaxation allows self-healing. Following the energy session(s), animals may begin to eat again, have less pain, heal more quickly and demonstrate increased confidence and joy.

Energy work does not replace medical or mental health treatment; it works in concert with the other choices you make about your health—medical treatment, counseling, nutrition, exercise, meditation, sleep. Energy therapy is one aspect of a holistic approach to living your healthiest life. In these pages, you will learn how to make informed energy therapy choices that support you in achieving your best life.

Ten years ago, I loved my life. Lloyd and I were comfortable and happy. My proposal writing and development business was rewarding and successful. We travelled and enjoyed activities with family and friends. Our Miniature Schnauzer, Zelda, and I volunteered at Providence St. Peter Hospital in the Animal Assisted Activities and Therapy Program.

Lloyd entered the hospital in November 2013 for a lung resection to remove cancer. An examination of the removed tissue showed the tiny mass was not cancer, but Bronchiolitis Obliterans Organizing Pneumonia. Complications followed, another surgery, and more complications. Despite the best efforts of the medical staff, he was left respirator-dependent, but mentally alert. Five-and-a-half months after the unnecessary surgery, at Lloyd's request, life support was withdrawn and he died.

Life as I knew it collapsed. I tried to re-create our life together, but it wasn't possible. The life I'd known shifted forever. I was adrift, frozen. Our dreams and my life plan died with him. I was alive, but without the zest that makes life worth living. My friends and grief support group gently held me. I struggled daily to move in ways that would tip my universe toward peace and away from grief, toward hope rather than despair.

The following year, my friend Jane decided to quit dialysis and medications and accept death. She gathered her family to say her final goodbyes. She hosted a wonderful reunion, full of laughter, pictures, and family memories. That evening she did not keep her dialysis appointment and did not take her medications. The crisis came. When I arrived the next morning, Jane lay on the floor in extreme agitation spewing angry accusations. Her family called hospice as planned, but the visiting nurse said hospice could not get involved because Jane was experiencing a psychotic break. She recommended the family call 911 and left.

Jane's sons picked her up and carried her to the living room couch. My sweet therapy dog, Zelda, and I sat beside her. Jane clutched Zelda and eventually calmed enough to move to her bed in the back bedroom. I spoke softly, using a guided imagery technique I'd heard thirty years earlier to take her to her favorite beach and feel herself warmed by the sun, lying on the sand, calm, relaxed, and peaceful. I felt an overwhelming compulsion to hold my hands about six inches above her body and move them slowly from above her head to below her feet.

Jane said the experience was like "going to Nirvana." She fell asleep and I tiptoed out. I visited Jane daily. I went into her bedroom, closed the door, and we talked until she tired. Eventually, she would ask me to run my hands above her body. When I did this, she became peaceful and drifted into sleep.

Five days later with death imminent, Jane's family gathered at her bedside. I moved my hands slowly over her body from above her head to below her feet, repeating the motion until she slept. Jane died shortly afterwards. Her daughter asked me where she could learn to do what I had done. I had no idea; I didn't know what it was.

I purchased a book on cancer treatment options for a friend with a recent terminal diagnosis. One chapter dealt with alternative therapies and included a paragraph on Therapeutic Touch. The text said that some people without training could do this work. My experience with Jane was so powerful I bought Delores Krieger's book, *The Therapeutic Touch: How to Use Your Hands to Help or to Heal,* and began reading it.

I took Krieger's book with me to read while I waited my turn at Providence Hospital to get the required annual tuberculosis test for volunteers. On the table beside me was a brochure for Healing Touch Level I training at the hospital that weekend. I called the coordinator and enrolled. I completed Level I and II in quick succession. I attended the Healing Touch practice sessions twice a month where we exchanged mini-treatments. I cried on the treatment table, releasing deeply held grief from Lloyd's death. So began the long healing process that changed my life, healed my grief, and allowed me to love, and be loved, again.

Within two years, I completed my Healing Touch certification, closed my proposal development and writing business, and launched my career as an energy healer. Once I experienced Healing Touch, I wanted to explore every aspect of energy medicine. My Doctor of Education degree in Leadership didn't prepare me for this new direction in my life. I earned my Reiki Master degree, studied Pranic

Healing, Matrix Energetics®, Reconnective Healing®, The Reconnection®, ThetaHealing®, EFT (Emotional Freedom Technique), and Access Consciousness®. Each method, commonly referred to as a modality, offered additional avenues for accessing this powerful healing resource. I learned and practiced Transcendental Meditation. I treated any person or animal that wanted a session. My clients were my teachers and my inspiration. I tended to my personal healing as I helped others find their healing.

I want to share with you the information I found by accident and exploration. Section One is about considering options. You'll find answers to: What is energy medicine? What research supports it? Who regulates it? Why would anyone choose it? What is it good for? Section Two discusses making choices. The use of energy healing for animals is discussed in more detail, including who's healing whom. The spiritual, mental, emotional, and physical aspects of energy healing are considered, as well as the concept of healing into death. Section Three focuses on healing ourselves and our desire to heal others. What to consider when choosing a practitioner is outlined. The role of angels and other beings in healing is discussed, as well as the challenging question: Do you want to heal others or change them?

Each chapter concludes with questions for reflection so you can explore your attitudes, beliefs, and experiences with healing and draw your own conclusions. The Resources and Recommended Reading section gives sources for the quotations and lists other materials you may want to consult.

Client names, details, and circumstances are changed to protect their identities. Privacy is maintained except in those cases where people have given permission for their experiences to be recounted or their experiences are already published. When referring to animals and their people, I used care person or caregiver as the designation rather than owner or guardian to avoid any negative connotations attached to these words. Animals received the same privacy considerations as humans.

This book is for you. Read it in any order you choose. Read what attracts you. The ideas presented are for your consideration. I am not offering medical advice or prescribing any method of treatment for physical or mental issues. Consult with medical professionals. Not every situation demands medical intervention, nor does every situation require energetic intervention. Energy therapy is a complementary modality that works with other healing options for prevention, maintenance, intervention, and end of life. Health decisions for your children, your animals and yourself are up to you.

There is much to explore in the world of energy healing; this is just the beginning. Let me be your coach and mentor as you consider expanding your options for improved health and well-being. Let me introduce you to the potential of energy therapy to transform and heal your life and the lives of those you love and care for, whether they are human or animal. If you have questions, concerns or healing stories you'd like to share, email me at wanda@WandaBuckner.com.

I am excited to share the world of energy healing with you and your animals.

Wishing you well now and always,

Wanda Buckner

Section One:

CONSIDERING OPTIONS

"The body heals itself. This might seem to be an obvious statement, because we are well aware that wounds heal and cells routinely replace themselves. Nonetheless, this is a profound concept among CAM* systems because self-healing is the basis of *all* healing."

--Marc S. Micozzi, *Fundamentals of Complementary and Alternative Medicine*

*Complementary and Alternative Medicine

Chapter One
CHANGING YOUR LIFE

Our lives move along at a steady and expected pace—education, employment, marriage, children—and then the unexpected happens. Chronic illness. Death. Divorce. Loss. Or something much less dramatic but just as life changing—knee surgery, job loss, children leaving home, retirement. You may want more—more joy, more love, more meaning, or less—less pressure, less effort, less fatigue.

We are all in transition. Our bodies, minds, emotions, and spiritual connection fluctuate daily. Our children race through childhood and youth. Our beloved animal companions are born, live, and die in a few short years.

TRANSFORMING: WHETHER WE WANT TO OR NOT

Energy sessions support our life force and boost self-healing from all manner of crises and changes. Healing occurs on every level—spiritual, mental, physical, and emotional. Energy from the universe flows through the practitioner, like a magnifying glass concentrates the sun's energy, to supplement our inner resources. This boost allows self-healing and integration at the deepest levels. When our energy shifts, our life shifts and the energy around us shifts. We transmute into more of who we are rather than withdraw into blame, anger, and hopelessness.

Perhaps you or your animals have undergone multiple medical tests and nothing is found wrong, but you know something isn't right. Or perhaps there is a diagnosis and medical and veterinary professionals are doing all they can and it's not enough. Or perhaps the interventions are enough, but your healing is slow, painful and difficult. The process depresses your spirits and weighs on your mind. Every day is a struggle. Now what?

A powerful healing life force permeates the universe. We see it in starfish regenerating a severed limb, animals licking their wounds to heal them, grass growing through concrete and cedars growing vertically from the trunk of a fallen tree. The healing power of energy has always existed and flowed through the hands of healers to people and animals. Healers in every culture have tapped into this force to help themselves, others, and animals.

You might wonder how people moving their hands above the body or placing their hands on joints and organs can make a difference. Sarah Wagner, DVM, explains, "The practitioner's energy field entrains the patient's energy field and changes its vibration, allowing the body's instinctive healing mechanisms to work more efficiently." The calm, even, ordered flow of energy from the universe positively affects the energy of the recipient and supports self-healing. The body's system comes into harmony with the energy of the universe to restore healthy energetic patterns.

WHAT IS ENERGY HEALING?

The energy therapy discussed in this book refers to practitioners interacting with the aura (also referred to as the biofield) that surrounds and permeates the body to bring about a positive change in the energetic flow within and around the body.

Every bit of matter is made of energy. These energy bits create mass. That mass has an energy field that extends beyond the physical shape we perceive. Sometimes we are aware of this energy field; but often, we are so used to feeling and being within or near the energy, we don't consciously recognize it, just as we are unaware we are in air.

Have you entered a forest and felt a physical change in your body and emotions? You are in the energy field of the forest as a whole and being influenced by its energy. We easily experience the difference between the energy in a natural forest and the energy in a busy shopping mall. Both have energy fields made up of the individual components and beings within the space. Miles of wiring, electrical and electronic devices, concrete, plastic, heating and cooling equipment, glass, sound, and the myriad people working, shopping and walking the corridors influence the energy field of a mall. Rain, sun, large and small trees, a variety of plants and fungi, earthworms, deer, birds, and all the species that live within the forest and visit it influence its energy field.

Each element of the forest (and the mall) has a unique energy field. Lean against a tree to experience its energetic vibration. The larger the element you choose, the easier it is to experience its field. Whether or not we are able to perceive it, every item—from a pebble to a hummingbird to an elk—has an energy field. Human eyes and senses often cannot distinguish these fields; often our scientific measuring instruments cannot either. In some objects, we can see the effects of their field, such as in the attraction of metal filings to magnets. When you hold a large crystal, you may experience a different feeling, emotion or image in your palm or body than when you hold a similar sized volcanic rock or seashell. People who work as energy healers cultivate their awareness of the energy fields of places, things, people and animals.

The term energy field is the broadest term and encompasses the term biofield, bioenergetic field and aura. Biofield and bioenergetic field have the same meaning and are sometimes used interchangeably with the term aura. The energy field of living beings is called a biofield. The biofield is a product of the energy of the organs, systems, and cells of the animal (including humans).

The biofield reflects the health of the animal because it is composed of the energy fields of each part of the living system. If a cell within the liver is damaged, its energy will be different from that of a healthy cell. Medical diagnostic procedures can identify clusters of cells that are atypical. The greater the number of atypical cells, the easier they are to identify by trained personnel looking at images. The larger the cluster of atypical cells, the larger the effect they have on the biofield. Energy healers may perceive these areas as hot, cool, congested, or tingly. Your hand may feel the heat (inflammation) of an injured knee a few inches away from the actual knee. You are feeling the energy of the injured area. The healthy knee will have a different feel.

The terms energy field, biofield, and aura are used interchangeably in this book. People who work with energy often use the word biofield because its meaning is more widely known. Our emotions affect the biofield/aura because chemicals released by the brain influence the systems and cells of the body, and reflect in our biofield. The energetic fields we are within and around, the emotions of others, our animals, everything we think about and come in contact with, influences our auras.

In a forest, your aura may be expanded and open; in a crowded mall, you unconsciously draw your aura close and tight. An animal's aura is proportionately larger compared to its body size than a human's. Because animals are often prey and predator, their auras are larger to sense danger or food in their territory. The human aura is traditionally illustrated with seven layers that correspond to the seven chakras. Energy healers may work within individual layers, but they influence the aura and body as a whole. Medical doctors address specific issues, like broken bones or arthritis or measles, and also influence the total body and energetic field.

Energy workers believe that just as what happens in the body affects the aura, what happens in the aura affects the body. Energy healers may clear the congested energy of unreleased grief. This clearing allows your energy to flow freely and bring balance back to your life. If the energetic pattern of atypical cells can be cleared and balanced, the cell can self-heal and return to its original healthy state. Similarly, trauma held in the body and aura, can be relieved and released through working with the energy field.

Hands on healers view the body, spirit, thoughts, and emotions as an energetic system that is in motion, each part influencing the other, as well as influencing, and being influenced by, the outer environment. The body exists within a complex electromagnetic field that reflects the body's disturbances as well as calm. Disturbances in the field over time can negatively impact the body and manifest as disease. To affect any part, is to affect every part. Energy healers clear and balance the energetic field, which in turn clears and balances our physical, mental, emotional, and spiritual aspects.

The Indian word chakra refers to the energy centers in the body. Energy workers may use the term energy center instead of chakra as a more understandable and acceptable term. When I came to energy work, I had no knowledge or concept of chakras. Anodea Judith, MD, in *Wheels of Life*, defines them as "organizing centers for the reception, assimilation and transmission of life energies." That concept was a leap of faith for me!

Judith's illustration of the location of the major chakras relative to the spinal nerves brought Western and Eastern viewpoints together. I saw the clusters of nerves positioned at each chakra (except the crown chakra at the top of the head). The seven major chakras for people and animals are the root chakra at the perineum, the sacral chakra in the lower abdomen, the solar plexus chakra at the physical solar plexus, the heart, throat and brow chakras, also at their physical locations and the crown chakra at the top of the head. Many other chakras are in the body and, according to some people, beyond the body. Some energy healing modalities refer to chakras, others do not.

HAYSTACK THEORY OF HEALING

We all have felt miserable and gone to bed to recover. Then an irresistible invitation comes. We pop up, get ready, go, and have a wonderful time, totally absorbed in the experience. When we return home, we descend into the doldrums again. What is that about? How can we manage our well-being so we are less dependent on external events? Why do some people consistently have health issues? They recover from one thing only to get another. Why are other people vibrantly healthy, despite exposure to the same challenging environment?

Our ability to deal with difficulties, challenges and change can be influenced through energy work. Energy therapy could be the catalyst that allows you to release disease, heal trauma, or ease your way into death. Energy work can clear long-standing physical, mental, emotional, and spiritual issues, and open new ways of being.

Illness, trauma, surgery, emotionally charged events, and many other life situations deplete our energy. Energy therapy boosts our system's ability to self-heal through deep relaxation, clearing, balancing, and replenishing our system. More than that, it can clear out-of-date beliefs and directives from other people or institutions that interfere with access to our knowing and our innate capacity for vibrant health, exceptional well-being, and a fulfilling life. If you are anxious about upcoming medical treatment, are not recovering from surgery in a timely manner, have unexplained pain, or dissatisfaction with your life, consider energy therapy. You have nothing to lose and it could make a huge difference.

Just like there is a "straw that broke the camel's back," there is a straw that heals the camel's back. We gather straws with the intent to heal—traditional medicine, meditation, exercise, complementary modalities—and at some point, one straw is the final straw. We heal.

CHOOSING SOMETHING DIFFERENT

You are unique and your experience with energy therapy will be unique. You are the expert on yourself—it is all about you, not about the practitioner, the doctor, the expert. You are the expert and the change agent. If you choose to change your energy and the energy around you, you can do it. *The Secret* and all the books and blogs that followed emphasize changing your energy through focusing on what is right with you and your world rather than what is wrong. Abraham, channeled by Esther Hicks, advises us to tell a little better story that moves us toward our vision. Tut, from Dooley's *Notes from the Universe*, reminds us to choose the good thoughts.

You may be at a decision point: "What can I do to improve my situation?" Perhaps you or someone you love, either human or animal, is experiencing a problem that isn't amenable to professional medical or mental health care. Perhaps professional intervention isn't achieving the results you want. Energy therapy does not replace medical or mental health care, but it does work in conjunction with them. Energy healing is a complementary treatment that supports individuals who also see physicians, naturopaths, chiropractors, and counselors. Energy work can also be a stand-alone intervention for issues that do not require medical or therapeutic intervention. Choosing energy work when we are healthy supports our body, emotions, and spirit to remain healthy and vital.

ENERGY THERAPIES

Because every particle of this universe is energetic, the term energy healing could be used to refer to all healing. Gary E. Schwartz, PhD, says, "From this perspective, herbs, drugs, physical manipulation, and even surgery, involve energetic processes in healing." We can narrow this very broad (but accurate) description to interventions that are clearly energetic. Lasers, light, sound and magnetic devices fall within this definition of energy therapy. Massage is sometimes called energy therapy because tension, energy held in the muscles, is released. Acupuncture opens the energetic channels (meridians) of the body.

The energy therapy discussed here refers to human practitioners interacting with an animal or human's chakras and aura to influence a change in the energetic flow within the body and in the field around the body. The examples given are primarily from the healing modalities I am most familiar with: Healing Touch, Healing Touch for Animals, Reiki, and Reconnective Healing. This is not to imply that other techniques, such as ThetaHealing, Pranic Healing, and Matrix Energetics, do not work. They do. I use these modalities as the situation dictates. Many other healing systems exist that I have not studied and more systems are undoubtedly on the way. For brief information on additional healing options, see *The Encyclopedia of*

Energy Medicine by Linnie Thomas. For in-depth information, go to the U.S. National Center for Complementary and Alternative Medicine on the Internet or explore the information in *Fundamentals of Complementary and Alternative Medicine.*

DOES ENERGY WORK, WORK?

John, my skeptical boyfriend, became convinced that energy healing works after his first treatment. I returned from an energy training excited to try the "Seven Layer Drain and Replace." I offered John a treatment. He agreed and stretched out on my treatment table. I stood at his feet and drained each of the seven layers of his aura, corresponding to the body's seven major chakras. He fell asleep during the treatment. We had no plans, so I let him sleep an hour before I woke him. He got up, but went into the bedroom and fell asleep again. After another hour, I woke him again. He moved into the living room, where he promptly fell asleep on the couch.

When I woke him the third time, he said, "You've drained all the energy out of me." I gasped! I had forgotten the final part of the technique—the replacement! I hustled him back onto the treatment table, stood at his head, and completed the technique, letting energy flow into his crown chakra and throughout his body. He got up from the table awake and refreshed. That experience made a believer out of him!

In my business—proposal development and writing—evaluation was a necessary part of every grant and program. Evaluation results told the grantor and the grantee what worked and what did not, and where changes were needed to improve results. I wanted similar feedback from my first clients. I wanted to know if the work I did made a difference. Even though I gave and received Healing Touch treatments during practice sessions bi-monthly for two years, I was not confident I could use the techniques effectively with strangers. However, the next step for Healing Touch certification was to provide and document 100 energy sessions.

In exchange for five free sessions, I asked my clients to complete an evaluation. The form included questions such as: To what extent was the issue you came for resolved? Were there unexpected benefits? Was the setting conducive to treatment (I worked from my home and had a dog)? Did I talk too much? Were the suggestions for self-care helpful? Fourteen clients with 68 total sessions responded to the survey.

My clients identified the issue or issues they had come to heal. They listed: old wounds, hand or knee injuries, anxiety, continuing pain, Irritable Bowel Syndrome, grief, insomnia, depression, binge eating, lack of relaxation, lack of connection to the world, life transition, job transition, and more. When asked to what degree their issues were resolved after five treatments:

• 29.5% reported the issue was 100% resolved.

• 43.8% said it was almost resolved.

• 29.5% said it was somewhat resolved.

I was amazed and delighted, but what really captured my attention was that 100% of the clients said they experienced other benefits. They listed:

• A sense of well-being that encouraged greater healing

- More energy
- Relaxation
- [Treatment] reached all levels
- Less anxiety
- Felt really cared for
- Spiritual sense of calm
- Released stored physical trauma
- Unlocked ability to laugh/cry
- Anger drain and heart healing

Medical doctors might say the placebo effect was responsible for the 29.5% who reported their issues 100% resolved. For me, the placebo effect is evidence of the body's ability to self-heal. The client responses validated the work. How many medical patients report that level of benefit? Deepak Chopra says surveys "have shown that as many as 80 percent of patients feel that their . . . reason for going to the doctor was not satisfactorily resolved when they left his office."

The 100 sessions were so rewarding, satisfying, and effective that I officially opened my Healing Energy Services business May 1, 2007. On August 1 of that same year, I permanently closed my proposal development and writing office.

THERE ARE ALWAYS OUTCOMES

As a new practitioner, I didn't understand the mandate to be detached from outcomes. After all, if clients didn't get better, they wouldn't come back! On the evaluation, a few clients said the treatments had 25% or less success in resolving their issue.

However, they added that the process was still worthwhile and they would do it again. All of the clients experienced unanticipated benefits. Instant healing is thrilling; however, people also heal in ways that are not immediately apparent and on their individual timeline.

Based on my clients' input, I refined my practices. I talked less and listened more. I kept the client's issue in mind as I worked, but trusted that healing took place on many levels. I learned the presenting problem was not necessarily the primary issue. I realized people could tell me anything they wanted, but didn't need to tell me anything at all. Instead of giving advice, I made more referrals to other health professionals.

Eventually, I let go of outcomes. If I was more invested in the client's healing than the client, the sessions were about my ego, not about the client. My clients' healing was self-healing. It was about them, not about me. Energy healing is not talk therapy. The magic happens on the table, not in the conversation.

Healing Touch and other biofield modalities can relieve pain, positively influence depression and anxiety, and much more. During a session, people often access deep feelings and integrate intellectual insights. Inner communication may open to resolve emotional and spiritual issues. Clients often feel cradled in the love of the universe. Routinely, they report deep relaxation, calm, and peace.

In a 1970's study of heart disease at Ohio University, rabbits ate an extreme high-cholesterol diet to study cholesterol's effect on arteries. As expected, the rabbits began to display symptoms as their arteries began to have blockages, except for one group, which had 60 percent fewer symptoms. Nothing was different in the protocol or in the rabbits' physiology. However, the student feeding those rabbits took the time to pet and hold each rabbit before feeding it. That one difference allowed those rabbits to resist the effects of the diet. Duplicate experiments with neutrally and lovingly treated rabbits resulted in similar outcomes. Perhaps this is part of the secret of energy healing. The personal relationship between the practitioner and the client allows clients to overcome the stressful influences in their lives. The healing act is a joy for the practitioner, as petting the rabbits was for the caregiver, and a buffer against negative effects, as it was for the rabbits.

I admire my clients' spiritual strength, internal resources, and personal wisdom. I continue to learn and grow from my experiences with clients. I am deeply grateful for the wonderful human and animal teachers that grace me with their presence.

For Reflection

1. Do you believe energy therapy could work?

_____

_____

_____

_____

_____

2. What did your parents believe about healing?

_____

_____

_____

_____

_____

3. What did their parents believe?

_____

_____

_____

_____

_____

4. What changed that contributed to the differences among your beliefs?

_____

_____

_____

_____

_____

Chapter Two
HEALING WITH ENERGY THERAPY

Energetic assessment and therapy is already in use in hospitals; however, machines, not humans, usually conduct these procedures. I always ask medical professionals, "How do you use energy medicine in your practice?" They pause. Then they begin to identify the myriad ways—laser, ultrasound, shock therapy, defibrillation, radiation therapy, nuclear medicine, pacemakers, TENS (Transcutaneous Electrical Nerve Stimulation) units. Energetic diagnostic tools are taken for granted—magnetic resonance imaging, electrocardiograms and electroencephalograms.

In *Energy Medicine: the Scientific Basis*, James L. Oschman lists the electrical frequencies, measured in Hertz (Hz equals one cycle per one second), needed for healing specific tissues. Two Hz boosts nerve regeneration; seven Hz positively affects bone growth; ten Hz improves ligament healing. He reports, "Not only are we documenting the presence of such [energetic] fields, but researchers are understanding how fields are generated and how they are altered by disease and disorder." The same range of frequencies found effective for tissue repair can be measured coming from the hands of energy practitioners.

"The rationale behind vibrational medicine is straightforward: diseases and disorders alter the electromagnetic properties of molecules, cells, tissues, and organs" (Oschman). Prior to modern medicine, humans used their hands, plants and prayers for intervention. We can do the same today.

ENERGY THERAPY DEFINED

Oschman hypothesizes, "When healthy tissue [the practitioner's hand] is brought close to such a [non-healing] wound, essential information is transferred via the energy field, communication channels open and the healing process is 'jump started.'" The client's energy entrains with the energy flowing through the practitioner, allowing the body to return to its ideal energetic balance for self-healing. This is the same principal as resonance. When one tuning fork is struck, a tuning fork of the same size and shape will vibrate as though it also were struck. Sympathetic resonance refers to a vibration in one item resulting in a vibration in a second item. Harmonic resonance refers to vibrations over multiple frequencies.

"Resonance is the foundation of all energetic communication. It is the fundamental process of connection and sharing, and the basis for how antennas work" (Schwartz). You may hear energy healers talk about tapping into universal energy or allowing healing energy to flow through them. All of these expressions speak of practitioners resonating with a healing stream that flows through them to the client. The client's energetic flow entrains with the healing energy for self-healing. In Reconnective Healing, the practitioner engages with frequencies of energy, information and light around and within the client. The frequencies do not flow through the practitioner; rather the practitioner is an observer of the process.

Carol Komitor, founder of Healing Touch for Animals, explains the physiology changes that occur as a human or an animal deeply relaxes during energy work. As the body relaxes, it releases endorphins, which further relax the muscles, allowing increased circulation. This increased blood flow elevates the oxygen levels, which allows increased nutrient absorption. This supports enzyme production, regulation of hormones, and toxin release leading to healthy cell growth that promotes healing and regulates the immune system.

SO MANY CHOICES!

The Internet lists thousands of energy therapy methods. How do you know where to start or what to choose? Energy therapies are classified as either complementary or alternative healing modalities. Alternative healing modalities take the place of traditional western medicine. Complementary modalities are used in conjunction with traditional medical intervention. The U.S. National Center for Complementary and Alternative Medicine (NICCAM) groups these therapies into five broad areas:

1. Dietary supplements,
2. Mind and body practices such as yoga, guided imagery and meditation,
3. Manipulative and body based practices that focus on the body and its systems, such as Rolfing and massage
4. Other CAM practices, including Tragor psychophysical integration; healers using indigenous traditions, and practices based on influencing and manipulating the biofield using magnets, light, sound, or the practitioner's hands (the focus of this book).

5. Acupuncture, homeopathy, and aromatherapy are just a few of the other modalities in use.

WHAT'S THE DIFFERENCE?

The same modalities available to support our well-being are increasingly available for the animals we live with. Some veterinarians now offer acupuncture, chiropractic care, laser treatments and/or nutritional counseling in addition to traditional care. Additional options for animals offered by non-veterinary practitioners include body-based methods such as massage and acupressure and energy-based methods like Reiki and Healing Touch for Animals.

Massage treatments provide the same benefits for people and animals—stress relief, tight muscle release, pain reduction, increased circulation and deep relaxation. Practitioners manipulate and apply pressure to our soft tissues to help us relax and heal. Practitioners must be trained in massage techniques, kinesiology, anatomy, physiology, and first aid. They are licensed by the state where they practice.

Acupressure is based on acupuncture. Acupuncturists manipulate the flow of qi (life force) through our meridians (energetic channels) using needles at specific points to correct imbalances and improve well-being. Acupressure has the same goal as acupuncture: to balance and restore the body's natural harmony. Practitioners do not need to be veterinarians. Acupressure can relieve muscle spasms, release natural cortisone to reduce swelling and inflammation, release endorphins to increase energy, relieve pain, support quicker healing of injuries, build the immune system, help relieve chronic health problems, enhance mental clarity and calm, and strengthen muscles and joints.

Reiki is a Japanese healing method founded by Dr. Mikao Usui around 1900. Reiki provides stress reduction and relaxation that also promotes healing. Reiki is based on the concept that life force flows through and around every living being. Our life force responds to and is influenced by everything in our environment. When our life force is disrupted, our health and well-being is affected. Practitioners place their hands on the person or animal (or hold their hands near or at a distance) and allow the Reiki energy to flow from a Higher Power through them to the client and go where it is needed. Practitioners may follow a pattern of hand placements or move their hands intuitively to different areas of the body.

Healing Touch is a gentle, heart-centered, biofield energy therapy that often results in deep calm and relaxation. Practitioners use their hands to clear, energize, and balance the human energy field and energy centers, which positively affects physical, mental, emotional and spiritual health. Healing Touch Program is endorsed by the American and Canadian Holistic Nurses Associations and is an accredited provider of continuing nursing education.

The descriptions of massage, acupressure, Reiki and Healing Touch indicate the benefits they offer overlap, although their approaches differ. Massage practitioners work with the physical body. Acupressure influences the energetic flow within the body through the meridians. Reiki and HTA practitioners work with the energy within and around the body. Acupressure uses specific points on the energy meridians. Reiki takes a general approach. HTA practitioners focus on the chakras and use specific protocols based on the presenting issue.

Massage practitioners have a similar training background due to state regulation. Acupressure is often taught in conjunction with massage. A number of organizations teach acupressure using the acupuncture points as the common basis for the curriculum. HTA, Matrix Energetics, ThetaHealing, Reconnective Healing, and other newer systems have parent organizations that offer a core curriculum and set standards for their instructors and practitioners. No single body oversees Reiki instruction or practitioner standards. As a result, there are a number of variations of Reiki. However, all practitioners are tuned to Reiki energy by a Reiki Master. Massage and acupressure are commonly used on horses, dogs, and other species that enjoy touch. Reiki and HTA are used on all species in any environment because hands on touch is not required.

Massage, acupressure, Reiki and Healing Touch for Animals complement physician and veterinarian work and complement each other. The use of one modality does not exclude the use of the others. For example, we would not hesitate to have a massage one week and a chiropractic adjustment the next week. Animals and people often receive increased benefit from a combination of modalities.

The 2007 U.S. National Health Institute Survey indicated 38% of Americans use CAM therapies. "According to the American Hospital Association, in 2007, 15%, or over 800 American hospitals, offered Reiki as part of hospital services" follow-up. Many of us seek out these treatments for our animals as well.

RESEARCH BASE FOR BIOFIELD THERAPIES

"Biofield Therapies: Helpful or Full of Hype? A Best Evidence Synthesis" by Jain and Mills, summarizes the results of 66 research studies on therapies such as Therapeutic Touch, Healing Touch, and Reiki. These studies showed "strong evidence for reducing pain intensity in pain populations, and moderate evidence for reducing pain intensity in hospitalized and cancer populations." The evidence for "decreasing negative behavioral symptoms in dementia and moderate evidence for decreasing anxiety for hospitalized and cancer populations" was moderate. The effect of these therapies on other factors, such as "fatigue and quality of life for cancer patients" or "decreasing anxiety in cardiovascular patients" was equivocal.

Allen M. Schoen, DVM, references Krieger's research: "Searching for the curative secret in simple touch, Krieger discovered that what counted most was whether or not the nurses *cared* (Schoen's italics) about their patients." When the nurse cared about the patient, the healing response was stimulated. People in the medical professions do care, but their time with patients is often limited by the constraints of the job. Energy sessions are typically an hour in length with the practitioner's full attention on the client.

Research on energy modality effectiveness is difficult because many variables in humans cannot be controlled. The Center for Reiki Research cites research done with rats by Baldwin and colleagues (2006, 2008). In a laboratory setting, Reiki (performed at a distance from the rats) significantly *reduced stress responses* relative to sham Reiki." Individuals suffering from depression and stress also responded positively to Reiki treatments (Shore, 2004).

Healing Touch and Reiki have a research base behind them that indicates human patients benefit from the intervention. However, most biofield modalities are building their research base. You can search on the Internet by the name of any therapy you are interested in "+ research," e.g., Matrix Energetics + research, and find the research that has been done on that modality.

Given such moderate praise, why do people seek out energy therapies? Most choose energy work based on their previous positive results, the experiences of their friends or families, a desire to use less invasive interventions, or dissatisfaction with conventional treatments. It doesn't matter what the research says; what matters is whether or not it works for us.

Although biofield therapies are helpful in many situations, you may find you don't get the result you desire. This is also true of other medical and complementary treatments. Humans and animals are affected by multiple physical, environmental, emotional, and mental factors that contribute to their well-being. The disease or issue may yield to a single brief intervention, or it may require multiple interventions over time. Sometimes the issue does not resolve. People still die of undiagnosed illnesses that baffle medical doctors.

Very few medical procedures and treatments work 100% of the time for 100% of the people. The same is true of energy work. Whether people choose surgery or energy therapy, what is important to them is whether the technique provides the outcome they want for their situation. It really doesn't matter if the intervention was successful for 99 people out of 100 if you are the hundredth person and do not get the results you want. The only outcome that matters is what happens to you. When considering energy therapy, keep in mind that you are unique. Your experience will be unique. This is both the beauty and the frustration of energy work.

ENERGY THERAPY SIMILARITIES

Remember the story from India of the blind men describing an elephant? The man who "feels a leg says the elephant is like a pillar; the one who feels the tail says the elephant is like a rope; the one who feels the trunk says the elephant is like a tree branch; the one who feels the ear says the elephant is like a hand fan. . . ." Each one is right; yet no one is wrong.

So it is with the universal healing force; it is enormous and can be accessed at many different points. Whether you access it through Reiki, Healing Touch, Reconnective Healing, prayer, or another modality is irrelevant. One point of access does not invalidate other access points. From a scientific perspective, "There is no single 'life force' or 'healing energy.' Instead, there are many systems in the body that conduct various kinds of energy and information from place to place" (Oschman).

Training is not necessary to tap into the healing force. There are gifted healers among us who "discovered" the healing energy flowing through them and there are healers who, through training and experience, "uncovered" the healing energy flow. People who are unaware of their healing gifts can learn about them through courses and practice. Those who know they have the gift can focus and hone their skills through education and exposure to multiple modalities.

Every class, teacher, and client contributes to the practitioner's understanding, openness, and ability to interact with the healing energy that surrounds us. Having said that, no matter who the practitioner is, all healing is self-healing. Cuts heal. Cells replace themselves. Micossi writes, "The body's ability to be well or ill is largely tied to inner resources and the external environment—social and physical—has an impact on this ability."

We all have the innate ability to heal ourselves and to facilitate the healing of others. However, not everyone wants to be a doctor and not everyone is called to be a healer. There are answers to our physical, mental, emotional, and spiritual issues that are not based on traditional medical practices. We are fortunate to have both Western and Eastern medical knowledge available to us. We are also fortunate to have noninvasive, low-risk, low-cost energetic interventions as options. You may choose treatment from any of these or all. Whatever you choose, seek out practitioners who are passionate about their work and view our amazing bodies with awe.

For Reflection

1. What is your personal experience with energy therapy?

_____

_____

_____

_____

_____

2. If you have had energy sessions, were the results what you hoped?

_____

_____

_____

_____

_____

3. What are your concerns about energy therapy?

_____

_____

_____

_____

4. Under what circumstances would you choose energy therapy for yourself or your animals?

_____

_____

_____

_____

_____

Chapter Three
HEALING A LITTLE; HEALING A LOT

Energy therapy is a good choice when what you are doing isn't bringing the results you desire at the pace you desire. Most people who explore energy healing already have medical care and pay attention to their health and well-being. They may also see chiropractors, acupuncturists, and other complementary practitioners. Energy healing clients take responsibility for how they feel and for being part of the solution. They often eat well, exercise, and engage in regular spiritual practices. Looking for answers to issues that don't resolve is often the driving force for investigating energy therapy.

Perhaps you see anxiety in your animal, or maybe you or your pet have continuing digestive difficulties. Perhaps you feel stuck and restless. If you have seen a doctor or taken your animal to a veterinarian and no medical issue is found, consider an energy session.

Healing can be instant, incremental, or transformational. Ron brought his friend for an energy healing session. Ron's nose was stuffy and he kept sniffing, so I offered him RC, a Young Living Therapeutic Oil Blend to inhale. As he sat in the chair, I did a brief clearing of his sinuses and throat before I turned to the client. Ron contacted me the next day to tell me he could sing again! He'd had something in his throat for over a year that he couldn't hack up or rinse out that prevented him from even carrying a tune. He was amazed and grateful that his throat suddenly cleared and he could sing again.

Energy therapy can address and clear emotional difficulties in both people and animals. Animals that are overly anxious, aggressive, uncooperative, don't fit in with the group, fearful, or fail to bond with their caregivers can often overcome these difficulties through energy therapy.

Alice was a beautiful greyhound who had completed her service to the racing profession and been adopted into a loving home. However, she was aloof and standoffish in the new environment. She was obedient, but not affectionate. She tolerated petting, but didn't appear to enjoy it. One session of energy work and a change in how her care person interacted with her—telling her how wonderful she was and rewarding her for desired behavior—brought them together into a close loving relationship. The nervous stomach of a young dog improved with the use of Young Living's Essential Oil Blend Di-Gize®, a few sessions of energy work to help his digestive processes self-heal, and increased leadership by his care person to help him feel secure.

Energy therapy is low risk. Adverse reactions are rare, and when they do occur, they are usually brief—less than 24 hours. Energy therapy is non-invasive—no swallowing, poking, or cutting. Compared to traditional medical care, the cost is minimal. At the least, you will experience deep relaxation; at the most, you may get results you didn't think possible. Many times, one session is sufficient. However, a series of three to five sessions can have exponential results. You have nothing to lose except a few dollars.

ENERGY THERAPY FOR EVERYTHING?

Listen to your self-talk—are you describing an energetic problem? Do you say you've been stabbed in the back or that your heart is heavy? Do you feel stuck, scattered, that you're dragging around, are beside yourself, or torn up? Do your friends say, "I feel disconnected. I can't get going. I'm a little disoriented. I'm falling to pieces. It kills me to think of what happened. It breaks my heart." These statements indicate energetic imbalance.

Energy therapy addresses a wide variety of situations; however, not every issue is solely energetic. Look to the simplest solution first. If you have an active dog that is obsessively chewing on himself and is not getting enough exercise, the first intervention for the dog is more exercise! If you cannot provide more exercise, find something else for the dog to do or chew. If the dog is getting enough exercise, is there a medical issue such as allergies to something in the environment or the food? Is there a staph or fungus infection? If the dog is getting sufficient exercise and has no medical problem, energy therapy might solve the obsessive chewing. It is certainly worth trying. Energy therapy could prevent your dog needing sedation.

Our environment exacerbates many of our aches. If you wake up every morning with a sore back, consider the age and quality of your mattress. Do you wake up feeling great after sleeping in a hotel? Maybe the problem isn't your partner, your children, your body, or your boss. It could be your mattress or your pillow. Would gentle stretching help your back? Would a change in your chair at work make a difference? Would taking more frequent breaks from your usual work position solve the problem? Would a chiropractic adjustment help? Would a new mattress and pillow help?

Many issues require multiple interventions, rather than a single solution. A self-chewing dog may need more playtime, an enriched environment, and energy work to relieve anxiety. If you have ongoing back and neck pain, you may need furniture that is more ergonomic, medical intervention, energy work, and a change in how you perceive and react to your world. A new job might help too. However, if you have difficulty with authority, changing jobs won't help. If you re-home your dog to a family that keeps it in a kennel most of the day, the chewing will not stop.

Do you say things like, "She's a pain in the neck," or "I wish he'd get off my back," or "Taking care of Mom is such a burden." These statements point to an energetic component to your backache. An energy worker can move that weight off your back. However, unless you make additional changes, such as how you respond to others, it is likely you will pick that weight up again. You may protest, "But it's true. So and so *is* a pain in the neck!" Really? Or just a pain in *your* neck? Attitude adjustment, self-help materials, energy workers, and counselors may help you reframe your situation or lead you to explore other options for dealing with the person.

CONSIDERING ENERGY THERAPY

If you are curious about energy therapy and its benefits, don't wait for a problem. Try it before you need it! You would not hesitate to get a massage; don't hesitate to try an energy session in a modality that interests you with a practitioner who appeals to you. During the session, you may or may not be aware of the energy that runs through you, see colors, pictures, or have muscle twitches. It doesn't matter. Energy healing is not about your experience on the table (although it's very satisfying to see colors and images or hear voices). Instead, notice what is different immediately after the session and in the days and months that follow.

Not all energy modalities are the same and not all practitioners are the same. If you are not excited about your results, try something and someone else. The same is true of doctors. Ideally, you meet your medical provider when you're well. Then, when you have a medical need, the doctor has a baseline of what health looks like for you. You select a doctor that you feel comfortable with and trust; the same is true of an energy practitioner. Just as you would go to a medical specialist for certain issues, you might choose a different energy worker for a different approach based on your current situation. One professional doesn't have to meet all your needs—physical, mental, emotional, or spiritual.

When you are under medical or mental health care for an ongoing issue, supplementing it with energy therapy to keep your energetic system clear and balanced often helps you achieve your healing goals faster. One of my first clients (a friend who was willing to let me work on her at no charge) was Jan. Jan was scheduled for right hip replacement surgery in two weeks. Her left hip was replaced the year before, and the whole thing was a miserable experience.

Prior to the first surgery, Jan broke out in a terrible rash that was difficult to resolve. After surgery, she developed a staph infection and had to return to the hospital. Her surgery site had to be opened, cleaned, and treated for three days before the incision could be closed again. She didn't want to repeat that experience! A few nights before Jan came to my "office"—a converted bedroom in my home—she had a disturbing dream about the upcoming surgery. She saw herself on the operating table waiting for the anesthesiologist. The surgeon opened a case of saws and told her she had to pay in advance for the saw.

Jan had a low-grade infection when she came to her first energy session. After the session, she said the experience was relaxing; she'd felt some warmth in her feet. That was it. No bells and whistles, no "Wow, That was tremendous!" However, by her next session, the infection had cleared. I saw her again immediately before surgery and in her hospital room following surgery, then three times for follow-up at her home. Jan's surgery and recovery went well. She experienced none of the difficulties she had with the first hip replacement. The surgery she dreaded gave her welcome relief from chronic pain.

CHOOSING ENERGY HEALING FOR CHILDREN

Energy work is appropriate for all ages. Small research studies report the benefits of Healing Touch for infants, children, and youth (www.healingtouchinternational.org). Sessions for babies, human or animal, are brief due to their smaller body size. Choose energy therapy for a child for the same reasons you choose it for yourself: to reduce stress prior to surgery or other challenging situations; to enhance well-being; to support healing; to solve an issue that does not require medical intervention; for support during a series of medical interventions or in conjunction with the work of other medical or mental health professionals.

Forrest was 18 months old when his Mom, Joy, brought him for Healing Touch energy work due to sleep issues. Despite the pleasant, supportive nighttime routine Joy had in place, going to bed and staying asleep was a nightly challenge for Forrest. Joy hoped a treatment would help him settle down to sleep at night. After I cleared and balanced Forrest's energy field, I showed Joy how to clear his field and suggested she add this to the evening routine.

Joy found that doing the energetic clearing just before lights out helped Forrest transition from his active day to quiet time and nodding off to sleep. When Forrest's Dad saw Mom "sweeping" Forrest's biofield with her hands, he laughed aloud. However, the routine worked and Forrest and his older brother Ronan fell asleep peacefully. A few days later, Dad confessed that when he tried to clear Ronan's energy field, Ronan got mad and starting grabbing his energy back, out of the air around him. He told his Dad 'Don't mess up my energy!'" Ronan could see and feel the difference in his parents' approaches.

James was a bright, healthy, friendly eight year old when his parents brought him for a general "improved well-being" energy session. They wanted to see if a session might clear a persistent body ache he complained about, but for which there was no physical explanation. One session of clearing and balancing James' biofield relieved his chronic ache.

Nick chose a hands-off modality, Reconnective Healing, for his energy session. He had just completed his first year of high school, which he described as the worst year of his life. His mother emailed the day after to tell me that Nick said he felt like his "old self" and that both of them felt very peaceful. Nick's experience that summer and the following year in school completely changed. His sophomore year was filled with friends and activities.

SAFETY FOR CHILDREN

When choosing energy work for your children, have a session from the practitioner yourself before scheduling a session for your child. Although your experience won't be the same as your child's (or of anyone else's), it will give you an indication of what the process feels like, how the practitioner interacts, the practitioner's approach and what information your child might need prior to the session to feel comfortable. Minor and vulnerable children's safety and comfort is a primary consideration during energy sessions. If a youth does not want an energy session, let it go. You may think it is just what your child needs, but an uncooperative or unwilling client generally will not have a healing experience.

With a minor child, the practitioner should invite you to be present. You can give children in their teens the choice of whether or not you are in the room during their session, but I recommend staying in the room with younger children. Nothing the practitioner does needs privacy. However, do keep in mind, that you are not the client. Let your child answer for her or himself and have the primary interaction with the practitioner. Unless you feel a need to intervene, wait until after the session to give additional information or ask clarifying questions.

Ask the practitioner if information given by the child or uncovered during the session will be discussed with you afterwards. Some practitioners treat information given by children when their parent is not in the room as confidential unless the child appears in danger of harming him/herself or of being harmed. Both you and your child need to know in advance whether session information is confidential. If you are not comfortable with information being confidential, make a different agreement with the practitioner and your child or find someone else. If child abuse is suspected, expect the practitioner to notify the legal authorities.

HEALING AT A DISTANCE

The client does not need to be physically present with the practitioner for healing to take place. Most practitioners offer distance healing (also called remote healing). Hands off healing is required in some instances, even though the practitioner is in close proximity to the client. The client may be uncomfortable when touched or does not want or tolerate touch. Moving around the client to touch various joints or chakras may not be possible due to IVs and monitoring devices.

Wild animals or animals touched only for sheering or medical treatment do not enjoy touch. Birds and fish must remain in their environments. In these cases, the practitioner works at a comfortable distance. Both the caregiver and practitioner observe the client's reactions and responses during treatment. In other situations, clients live too far away to travel to the practitioner or for the practitioner to travel to them. Whether the distance is three feet or three-thousand miles, it doesn't matter. Healing travels across time and space just like starlight.

Practitioners use a variety of methods to facilitate distance healing. Some practitioners ask that the care person be present with the animal client to note behavior during the treatment. Human clients may be asked to lie down at the treatment time so they can actively participate in the session by observing their inner experience. In these methods, the practitioner makes an appointment with the client. The practitioner and client complete a phone intake prior to the treatment, then the client lies down (or the animal is observed by the caregiver) during the treatment. At the conclusion of the session, the practitioner and client discuss the session, including the practitioner's findings and the client's responses.

Some practitioners do distance treatment sessions at a time convenient to them, and let the client know after the fact that the session is complete. These sessions can be done without disturbing the client's daily work or routine. Practitioners send a follow-up report to the client.

When facilitating a distance session, practitioners may use a surrogate, such as a stuffed animal or doll, another person or animal, or themselves, and proceed with the treatment as if the surrogate were the client. Other practitioners visualize the client during treatment or use a photograph or line drawing to represent the client. The method is not important. The practitioner brings the same training and experience to each session, whether the client is physically present or not.

Many clients prefer to meet the practitioner in person prior to having distance sessions. They want the information they can gain in person from body language and affect, rather than relying solely on emails, phone conversations, or websites. However, face-to-face meetings are not always practical, though services such as Skype make it more so.

There is no difference in outcomes between being present with the client or working at a distance. Some practitioners primarily do distance work due to their location relative to their clients' homes. Other practitioners prefer distance work because they do not have a formal office and they can do treatments at hours more convenient to their schedule.

Distance or remote healing has the advantage of allowing practitioners to work without the distraction of the physical attributes and behaviors of their clients. Not being face-to-face with the client allows practitioners to focus from their spiritual or higher self directly with the client's higher self to clear deeply rooted issues. Most practitioners offer both distance and in-person sessions. The fee is the same whether by distance or in-person, unless there is a charge for travel time to the client's home.

TAKING CHARGE OF YOUR EXPERIENCE

Although many people experience physical sensations, emotional moments, cognitive shifts or spiritual revelations, you may not. What you experience during the session is not indicative of the healing that occurred. On the practitioner's treatment table, you may experience nothing different from what you would experience if you laid down in midday without falling asleep. This does not mean the healer is not facilitating the session appropriately or that you are blocking or resisting the experience. You may have a multi-dimensional experience one time, and feel and see nothing the next time. You may even fall asleep and snore. You might cry; you might laugh. Each experience may be different from the one before.

Healing can occur below your conscious awareness and continue to unfold in your life. Before you judge your experience or the healer, notice what is different for you over the next few weeks. Then decide if you feel you would benefit from another session.

Just like treatments such as counseling and traditional medical care, healing is not guaranteed. Some clients have results they consider miracles; other clients may be ho-hum about their experiences. Either way, children, parents and friends may see changes the client does not see. Clients can be unaware of changes because the differences may be subtle and so fully integrated into who and how they are, that they don't feel different.

While it is very validating and rewarding, for both you and the healer, for you to have an experience on the table, as Dr. Eric Pearl of Reconnective Healing says, even not having an experience is an experience.

For Reflection

1. Do you, your child, or your animal have a non-medical physical, emotional or mental issue you have decided to live with because you feel nothing can be done?

_____

_____

_____

_____

2. How would your life, or your child or animal's life, be different if this issue were no longer present?

_____

_____

_____

_____

_____

3. When scheduling a consultation with an energy worker, what questions would you ask?

_____

_____

_____

_____

4. Do you have a special connection across space with someone in your life? What does this connection have to do with energy healing?

_____

_____

_____

_____

5. Do you believe in the power of prayer to heal? Do you consider prayer to be distance healing?

_____

_____

_____

_____

Chapter Four
HEALING ON MULTIPLE LEVELS

Energy therapy can give the body the boost it needs to heal fully from medical procedures or traumatic injuries. Elgin had a septoplasty and bilateral turbinate reduction but continued to struggle with breathing issues following the surgery. A session of energy work with the specific intention to clear and soothe the nasal passages solved the problem. He wrote, "I have and am still able to breathe quite well through my nose since I left you. I hadn't been able to do that after the septoplasty and bilateral turbinate reduction."

HEALING PHYSICALLY

In 1984, while completing my doctorate and education administrative credentials, I developed iritis, an extremely painful eye condition. I felt like I had been stabbed in the eye and the knife was still sticking in it. In addition, I had excruciating back pain. The iritis led to finding the reason for my chronic back pain. I had ankylosing spondylitis, an arthritis characterized by inflammation of the spine and sacroiliac joints. With aggressive medication for the iritis and maintenance medication for the ankylosing spondylitis, my eyes recovered and my back pain became tolerable. Completion of the doctorate, a job change, and a new partner decreased the pressure on my body and spirit.

At the time I suffered from recurring iritis and significant back pain, I did not know about energy medicine. I thought traditional western medicine and gutting through the pain were my only options. I accepted daily medication as a necessary part of my life. However, after I began practicing and receiving energy work, I discovered I no longer needed the prescription anti-inflammatory and muscle relaxant. Today, there is no evidence that I ever had ankylosing spondylitis even though I have the genetic blood marker, the extremely dry skin, and experienced the iritis associated with the disease.

A randomized study of coronary artery bypass surgery patients conducted by Arom and MacIntyre showed "significant differences in a shortened length of stay for those in the Healing Touch group and a significant decrease in anxiety." Anecdotal reports of faster healing with energy therapy are found in most books about energy work. Joyce Morris, in *Reiki: Hands that Heal*, reports that Mary, who was told her broken arm would be in a cast for six to eight weeks, healed completely in 11 days. Four-year-old Martin's broken collarbone healed in five days with the help of distance treatments. Multiple Reiki treatments helped 16-year-old Harry's broken arm heal within 10 days. Morris' book contains many more examples of the value of Reiki for a variety of conditions.

Practitioner Garski, RN, reports on the Reconnective Healing website, "My patients are gradually having reductions in medications…Also, [hospital] stays have been dramatically shortened in chronic clients. These results are documentable and not subject to supposition as these patients have a 20-30 year database to base this statement on."

Sue had a blockage in her left carotid artery, discovered two years before, and was regularly rechecked by her doctor. She dreaded her upcoming check-up, anticipating more bad news. She scheduled a Healing Touch session with me prior to her doctor's appointment. When she received the results of her check-up from her doctor, she wrote:

> I just had to share this wonderful news with you, it is so very unexpected. This morning, I got the result of the sonogram on my carotid arteries. My doctor was shocked! The report is NO BLOCKAGE in either the right or the left artery. (The left was 30% blocked when I had the original sonogram done 2 years ago.) Disbelieving what he was seeing, he called the technicians who performed the sonogram. They had used a different procedure and a different technology, so he was uncertain as to how the two tests really compared. When going through all of the "pictures," the left artery still showed some plaque attachment, but no blockage, so he conservatively has said that the results are probably improved and certainly no worse than the original test showed.

> My doctor, an expert in this field, told me that I was the first patient he has ever had that had a follow-up sonogram come back better than the original. Now, I will admit to you that two years ago, I was part of a six-month study of a new drug intended to remove blockages from arteries and that probably has something to do with these results, since I am fairly certain I was not on the placebo. However, that

study continues and the actual results will not be known for some years. My doctor was stymied as to how good my result is, since, even with his conservative views it still exceeds anything that he thought possible from my taking the test drugs.

I honestly believe that Healing Touch had something to do with these unexpected results. I was just hoping that things had not gotten worse, and am delighted with this news. Relieved!

Did the energy work make the difference? Yes, I believe so. I also believe everything else Sue did made a difference too. She participated in a study on treating blockages, she dealt with her anxiety and negative anticipation, and she received energy work.

Crystal contacted me because her freshwater fish were dying. She worked with an expert on water quality and did what he recommended to bring the nitrate level in the tank into balance, but her fish continued to die. She buried 11 of her fish friends; she didn't want more of them to die. When I began the session, the remaining 23 fish turned toward me. The bolder ones watched directly. Others came from their hiding places to peak through the latticework of the structures in the aquarium.

I used energetic techniques to clear the aquarium water, then cleared and balanced the fishes' chakras. As I worked, the fish became brighter; their colors reflected the infusion of energy. Crystal said at one point, the fish seemed giddy, as if they were on a sugar high. Their attention fascinated me as I did the work. By the end of the treatment, the fish seemed revived. The water and the fish were energetically clear and balanced.

However, the high nitrate level had weakened the larger fish to the point they were unable to recover from the damage. Healing Touch supported the ability of the remaining fish to recover.

I wish this was the end of the story. However, the aquarium heaters stopped functioning properly and more fish died. The environment wasn't conducive to life for tropical fish and the energy work could not overcome it. Crystal bought and returned heaters until she found a combination that held the water at the required temperature.

HEALING MENTALLY

Tawnya suffered a traumatic brain injury (TBI) that instantly changed her life. Almost nine months after her injury, a brief complementary energy session at the Washington State Traumatic Brain Injury conference seemed to allow her brain to reorganize. After the conference, Tawnya wrote to tell me that after the treatment, she could filter out noises in a crowded area; remember what she was supposed to do; write, type and use full, interesting sentences. She was much happier and at peace with her new self. She had no headache and was not so overwhelmed. Her sense of humor had returned, as had her intimacy with her husband. Her old personality was coming back. Tawnya had been open-minded about the possibilities of energy work and was very grateful for the treatment. For the first time, she felt she would make a full recovery.

That session was the straw that healed the camel's back, but not the only straw. In 2013, she was a speaker during a breakout session at the same conference. In her words:

Four years ago, I sustained an assault to the head, which caused me to have a TBI (Traumatic Brain Injury). This began a journey that would be complex and indescribable. I was a woman in my mid-thirties at the time. I had everything going for me. My three children were still adolescents. I was happily married. I was financially doing well. I loved my job working with children with mental challenges and high risk of the juvenile system. The help and inspiration I gave these kids and their families was very fulfilling.

One day it all changed. The child I was working with had an episode and was totally out of control. His caregiver forgot to give him his morning medicine that really helped him therapeutically. In the midst of his manic episode, he managed to kick me square in the forehead. I was knocked 'silly' and left dazed and confused.

I had to relearn how to read, write, speak, and to accept the way I was and would be for the rest of my life. I used alternative therapies like Reiki, meditation, vitamins, vision therapy, and Reggae music. These helped me with my depression, Attention Deficit Disorder, memory problems, speech problems, anxiety, and my acquired Tourette Syndrome. I did the "Moving On" workbook with Penny's group at the Tacoma Area Coalition of Individuals with Disabilities (TACID). It helped me make mind maps to help navigate my road to recovery. My team consisted of me, supportive family and friends, my medical doctor, a lawyer, neurologist, speech and vision therapists, a neuropsychologist, vocational rehabilitation, and support groups.

I surrounded myself with those who understood me. I lost friendships and family relationships because they couldn't understand. Having a brain injury is very isolating because no one can see your impairment, and people don't understand. Having a loving and supportive environment is such a gift to someone with a brain injury. Love is what heals. The power of love is able to heal the energy in our bodies.

Tawnya is now the Board President of Brain Energy Support Team and has two businesses: Emergent Distributing and T Town Body Treatments. She is also a mentor to others who have experienced TBIs.

Jonathan came to my office for an energy session for his medically diagnosed clinical depression. His current treatment included medication and psychotherapy. When we met, he was unable to attend high school. He spent his days and nights in his bedroom on the computer. He wanted to feel better, but was in despair, at times even suicidal. The only possibility left seemed to be ECT (electroconvulsive therapy), which he wasn't keen on. Jonathan responded briefly to my questions before the session and didn't say much afterwards. I was surprised when he decided to have a second session.

He told me later that the sessions calmed and relaxed him, sometimes for as long as three days. Living even a few hours without the overwhelming depression he'd felt for the last four years was hugely important. Jonathan was accepted into a National Institutes of Health in-patient project researching the efficacy of a new medication for those diagnosed with Major Depressive Disorder. Years later, he told me the energy work was key in bridging the time between application and acceptance.

After seven difficult months on the in-patient unit that included getting off all prescription medications, then using the trial drug or a placebo, then repeating the process, the project trials were complete. Jonathan was discharged with prescriptions that counterbalanced his despondency. He left the facility able to use his existing skills, learn new information, and be self-supporting. Energy work didn't cure Jonathan, but it gave him hope so he could find the way to his healing. In the process, he helped hundreds of others who reaped the benefits of the research findings.

HEALING EMOTIONALLY

Healing is different for every being. A dog may have a limb amputated or use a roller cart and be as happy as when his body was whole or the dog may not adjust. The same is true of humans. The body may be cured, but the emotional, mental, or spiritual self may not be in alignment with the result. In these cases, energy therapy can be the catalyst for bringing the reality of what exists into alignment with what the body is now. The support of a mental health therapist, a loving family, and/or a spiritual advisor may also be part of the healing.

Tucker was a young cocker spaniel from a reputable breeder. He had a loving, well-informed care person familiar with the intricacies of taking care of cocker spaniels. I met Tucker at the request of his holistic veterinarian.

Tucker would not let anyone touch him except "his person" and even then, only in certain ways and certain places. He was a very handsome spaniel, and on the surface looked the picture of health. Unfortunately, his breeding had resulted in physical deformities that interfered with his life. His care person felt so badly for him that she babied him with food, so Tucker was overweight. That made his physical difficulties more challenging, and he was losing bladder control at night. He needed a veterinary examination. I wondered what happened to sweet Tucker that he felt he had to protect himself from everyone. He was not a dog with a difficult background. His care person had known him from a few weeks old.

I met Tucker in the veterinary hospital's comfortable examination room. The veterinarian, technician, and I sat on the floor with Tucker, who tried to hide behind his person. I cleared his energetic field from a short distance, and then moved so I could touch him. I balanced his energy with my hands on his body. During the process, some internal switch flipped from where it had been to the opposite position. Tucker stretched his head up and slobber-kissed my ear. Then he kissed his caregiver. He kissed the veterinarian. He was so happy. When he left the examination room, he greeted the reception staff with his whole body wagging.

Tucker received a second hands on energy treatment at his next veterinary appointment and let the veterinarian examine him. On his third visit, he happily accepted a chiropractic adjustment. He wiggled. He cuddled. He kissed. He was a changed dog!

I did the same basic Healing Touch treatment I've done many times with other animals. If his person had asked if this treatment would change her dog from a "you can't touch me anywhere" to a loving, responsive dog, I would have replied that it was worth a try. I might have recommended environmental changes and training protocols in addition to the work.

We will never know why he felt as he did, and we will never know why the simple act of balancing and clearing his field made such a difference in his disposition. He quit wetting inside the house, his care person is helping him lose weight, and his veterinary chiropractor helps him with his continuing physical challenges. All the people who meet Tucker love him and he loves them back.

Hanging on to a past event, whether it was wonderful or horrific, as if it happened yesterday, prevents us from experiencing our present life in its fullness. If your spouse died twenty years ago and you continue to cling to that event, your life will be filled with sadness. If the winning touchdown pass you caught in high school is the most dramatic and exciting thing that happened to you this decade, you need some new adventures! The best part of your life is not over; it's now. Your only life is now.

HEALING SPIRITUALLY

Spiritual healing and growth continues throughout our lives. This is true for people with no conscious spiritual practices and those with daily, purposeful spiritual observances. Energy healing provides us with greater access to our knowing and connection with the universe. A deeply devout client reported feeling "deep peace in my body, a lot of energy. I felt profound shifts, realignment to earth. In many ways, I feel more solid, more hopeful, an effortless knowing in myself. What will be will come to me as an unfolding."

In Reconnective Healing, the practitioner engages with the frequencies of light, information, and energy that surround the client and observes the client's involuntary reactions (called registers). Following the session, the client describes the experience and the practitioner records what the client reports. No discussion of the experience follows. Each client's experiences are unique from those of other clients and from one session to the next.

At 69, Opal felt the press of time. She came to energy work looking for answers. She was deeply immersed in volunteer work she was passionate about. Like most non-profit agencies, the one where she volunteered raised money through bazaar sales to support its cause. Opal was creative, hardworking, and completely committed to helping in every way she could. However, in the last year or so, she noticed she felt more and more pressed for time; her hands were always busy making items to sell to raise money for her favorite charity. She was frustrated because she never accomplished all she meant to in a day. She felt more driven than fulfilled.

Opal described her Reconnective Healing session:

> I began with a nice scene/picture of Mother Mary, like I was back in church. Very pleasant. Then back with mother and father. I could faintly smell his pipe. Nice to be with them. I felt myself enclosing myself with a golden light. I saw my heart opening up and keep opening and opening. Then I saw myself with a group of people, like nomads, with shawls and robes by a body of water, long ago, enjoying time by the water watching the waves wash up on the shore. We had a very simple lunch—apples, cheese,

bread. I was enjoying our time together. Then, I was with my brothers, sisters, nephew, and niece, all of them passed over. When I was with them, it was just light. I enjoyed being in their spirit presence.

Since that session, Opal concentrated more on creating unique sculptures for family and friends, allowing the objects to come together over time rather than driving herself to complete them. These beautiful sculptures, made primarily of found objects and recycled materials, bless the people and animals who receive them. Each one is a gift of love and good will, and raises money for her charity too.

With Reconnective Healing, you do not have to be concerned about whether the practitioner is a "pure" or "clear" channel for the energy. Your experience and its interpretation are completely your own. You remain the expert on yourself. Most energy healers do not have a medical or counseling background and do not have the training to take on either of these roles. Because you do not discuss your issues with the practitioner, you maintain your privacy and you do not receive advice from someone not qualified to give it.

After his third and final session, Lewis said, "I am breathing easier. I have a knowing that my heart is healed. [I feel] calm, joyful, no worries. Everything in its place." Helena described her experience: "A horse is running very, very fast. I'm being carried along; it's a big cat, then a wolf. I got the sensation its nose was right near mine, sniffing me. The wolf lay down and wrapped himself around me. I got a sense of being taken care of and a really clear message, then the sensation of being light in a tube full of light. I was hovering in the light; enveloped in light. 'Trust what you love.' Those were the words." The healings were complete; Lewis and Helena were in balance. Any discussion either before or after these sessions was superfluous.

HEALINGS ARE BETWEEN YOU AND THE UNIVERSE

Healing is between the client and the universe, not the client and the practitioner. The doctor sets the broken bone, but the body knits it together. Thus the expression—all healing is self-healing. All healers have stories of wonderful results.

Will you and your loved ones have the same results? There is no guarantee. You are unique and your experience will be unique. Healers work for the greatest good of the client, realizing we do not know what that is. We often also work with the intention to address the particular issue the client presents. My experience is that the presenting issue isn't always the most important one.

Sometimes, healings are "unintentional" as in this case:

> The first time I saw Wanda, she asked if I had any issues with my feet and if my shoes fit correctly. My feet and hands were always very cold—I wore long sleeves, long underwear, and wool socks to keep warm. I had been on chemotherapy for several years to control pustular psoriasis. After a few sessions, I realized my hands and feet were no longer cold! Although this wasn't the focus of our sessions, it's very nice to be toasty warm.

Margaret had a long history of difficulties, diagnoses, and interventions. In describing her Reconnective Healing experience, said it was if there was an oval of twelve people around the treatment table supporting her—like being an Eskimo child in the center of a huge skin held by others. She felt like a child tossed into the sky and loving it. She felt incredibly supported. Was she cured and suddenly free of the challenges in her life? No. However, the experience was healing for her due to the support and ease she felt during the treatment. Did it cure her circumstances? No. It did help her be more comfortable in the world and realize she was not alone.

For Reflection

1. Have you or someone you know experienced a spontaneous, unexplained recovery?

_____

_____

_____

_____

2. To what do you attribute the healing?

_____

_____

_____

_____

_____

3. If you could have any change in your life you wanted, what would it be?

_____

_____

_____

_____

4. What results would indicate to you that an energy session was successful?

_____

_____

_____

_____

Section Two:

MAKING CHOICES

It is reasonable to expect the doctor to recognize that science may not have all the answers to problems of health and healing.

--Norman Cousins, *Anatomy of an Illness:*
As Perceived by the Patient

Chapter Five
HEALING ENERGY AND ANIMALS

Many veterinarians and animal caregivers want alternatives to western medicine for the animals they live with or treat. Dr. Donna Kelleher's autobiographical book, *The Proof is in the Poodle: One Veterinarian's Exploration into Healing*, traces her journey from childhood, when she cared for animals and helped her neighbor weed her medicinal plant garden and make salves and teas, through veterinary school, her transition to a private practice, her marriage, and the death of her beloved dog.

Kelleher put into words what I believe and have observed. "For fractures, intestinal blockages, dehydration, or bloat, conventional veterinarians served a vital role in saving animals. But there were others [animals]. . . .that were capable of healing on their own with a subtle nudge in the right direction." Kelleher uses acupuncture, chiropractic, and western herbs; I use biofield energy modalities, but the concept is the same. We can support animal healing in a variety of ways. Some methods are less invasive with fewer negative side effects. Some methods work better in certain situations. I highly recommend Kelleher's sensitive portrayal of her struggles with ethical conflicts in practicing as a western-only veterinarian and her decision to take a different path.

Sue used distance Healing Touch to help a cat recover from life threatening wounds. The caregiver recognized the positive impact of the energy work, but didn't tell her veterinarian about the energetic assistance that helped the cat make such an amazing recovery. Perhaps the veterinarian would have dismissed the idea of energy healing, but perhaps not. An opportunity for expanding the veterinarian's awareness was lost.

Calico is a healthy hen that became broody—she decided to hatch the eggs she laid. Since there was no rooster and the eggs were gathered daily, there were no future chicks to incubate. However, Calico insisted on sitting on the nest. Calico's care person picked her up and put her on my lap. I put my hands on her and used the Healing Touch behavior change protocol to tell her she had a new job—to police the grounds and keep the bug population down. After five minutes or so, Calico had enough. She jumped off my lap and walked away. Calico stopped her broody behavior, went back to laying an egg a day, and now patrols the grounds for insects. The caregiver, a mental health professional, enjoyed a good laugh seeing me do what he called cognitive behavioral therapy with a chicken. However, he agreed it worked.

LIFE THREATENING PNEUMONIA—SIERRA

Marsha writes of her and her dog Sierra's experiences melding Western, Eastern and energy work. Although this account references me, similar accounts are common among the clients of energy healers. I share these stories to give you a sense of the power of energy work. Go to any energy healing modality or practitioner website for testimonials about the effectiveness of the work.

This summer Sierra, who was 13½ at the time, became seriously ill. He had mega-esophagus, organic matter stuck in the esophagus, stomach ulcers, and pneumonia from aspirating regurgitated stomach fluid and saliva. I took him into Summit Referral Hospital for acute care on August 23. At that point, we didn't know all that was wrong with him. We just knew that he was in pain, weak, unable to hold down even the smallest amounts of water, and panting so hard I was afraid of stroke or heart failure.

The vets at Summit began working on him but, over the next two days, he went further into himself and became weaker. By Saturday, no one thought he was going to make it. However, I could tell he was fighting. He wasn't ready to go yet and I felt my commitment to this dog was to help him live if he wanted to live. I told my regular vet, Dr. Martin, that I felt Sierra's Chi. Though his affect was deadened, he was fighting.

On Saturday, August 25, Dr. Martin did a session of acupuncture with Sierra at Summit. She was very concerned about how inward Sierra had turned and felt we needed to give him support. Dr. Martin told me that Wanda should be contacted (she had seen Wanda pull other animals back from the edge she saw Sierra sitting on). Over the next few weeks, Wanda did a number of both in person and remote energy treatments on Sierra.

Sierra was in doggy ICU with 24-hour care for eight full days. After he came home, all of his vets and many techs told me they didn't expect him to survive. These people deal with the sickest of the sick animals, and they all expected he wouldn't make it. Within a short time after

Wanda's first energy treatment, I saw Sierra start to come back. The vets told me the night after Wanda's first in-person treatment Sierra rested better and slept longer than he had since he arrived. The next day, he held his head up on his own, also a first, and coughed up a great deal of the junk from his lungs first thing. His eyes were more expressive than they had been.

Over the next day or so, with Wanda's treatment complementing the Western medicine, Sierra's lungs became clearer, his eyes brighter, and he became more engaged with what was going on around him. He tried to get up and move. He was interactive with me, listening to what I said. From that point on, every time Wanda worked on Sierra, I saw a marked jump forward in his improvement.

I know that Sierra would not have survived had Wanda not been an integral part of his healing team. Her work pulled Sierra back from the edge and provided him with forward momentum. Her work supported the Western work, supported Sierra, and provided him with the strength to help him help himself. I've never seen anything like it.

When I brought Sierra home, he could barely stand on his own. A walk for him was fifteen feet into the yard and back. Every time Wanda did healing work on Sierra, I saw benefits within hours, including increased chi, determination to move/walk further, better sleep, and, ultimately, clearer lungs.

What was interesting for me, though, was the stress relief I felt, just being within the realm of Wanda's work. I've seen Sierra go from "probably not going to make it" to walking with a spring in his step for two miles, wagging his tail constantly, and eating and sleeping very well. Energetically—he's a star!

REFUSING FOOD—GEORGINA

Sherry called me because her beautiful 11–year-old Persian cat, Georgina, was not adjusting well to the new home she and her husband moved to after they married. Sherry and Georgina had moved multiple times during the past two years, but this move was the hardest. Sherry had moved almost everything out of her old apartment into the new house two hundred miles away. Georgina stayed at the apartment for three days while Sherry set up their new home. Georgina was well cared for by a friend who came regularly to feed and pet her; however, she refused to eat or drink. When Sherry returned, Georgina lay limp on the floor.

At her new home Georgina continued to refuse food, pottied inappropriately, and passed very hard stools. Georgina's veterinarian examination showed she was a little anemic and had a slightly elevated white blood cell count, but otherwise her blood work was normal. At a loss for what to do, Sherry tried energy work.

Lavender essential oil helped Georgina relax during the Healing Touch energy session. The session cleared and balanced her energetic system, opened the energy flow in her spine and calmed her stomach and intestines. Georgina resumed eating, her elimination issues resolved, and she regained the lost weight. Energy work supported Georgina's system so it could self-heal from the trauma of the extended time alone and the move.

SURGERY SUPPORT—JACQIMO

Just as in humans, energy work appears to help those who have surgery experience an easier recovery. Jacqimo, a sweet toy poodle, required knee surgery—the kneecap on the right rear leg would not stay in place. The previous year, Jacqimo had the same surgery on his left rear leg and it did not go easily. This time Nancy decided to support Jacqimo with energy work. He had a pre-surgery energy session, energetic support during surgery and a post-surgery clearing to help move the anesthetic out of his system. The surgery went well.

Having energy work during surgery is similar to holding a patient's hand during a crisis. Deepak Chopra says, "You can grasp the patient's hand at a difficult moment in surgery and see the monitors for blood pressure and heartbeat register the calming effect."

When Jacqimo returned home, his recovery from surgery was slow. He was sluggish, almost dazed. He refused food and water and was not easily toileting. Nancy brought Jacqimo for two more sessions of energy work to help clear the after-effects of surgery and support his body to self-heal. Jacqimo's bodily functions returned to normal and he began using his leg soon after. Both Nancy and Jacqimo's veterinarian were amazed and delighted with how quickly his leg healed.

LIMITATIONS OF ENERGY HEALING

Temple Grandin dramatically improved animals' experience in slaughterhouses by looking at the environment from the animals' point of view. She also opened a new window on how animals think by relating the similarities between how she thinks to how animals think. Grandin is autistic. She sees and understands the world through highly specific, visual images rather than generalized concepts. She believes animals see the world the same way.

Her book, *Animals in Translation: Using the Mysteries of Autism to Decode Animal Behavior*, is a fascinating read. Grandin is a realist, not a romantic. She recognizes the co-development of humans and animals and our part in how animals behave today. She points out the shortcomings of genetic breeding, where breeding for a specific trait results in unintended consequences such as roosters killing hens or dogs born dangerous.

Grandin's work makes a distinction between behaviors that are hard-wired and those that are learned. We cannot erase hard-wired behavior, such as chasing prey; however, what to chase is learned. Care people and energy workers should be aware of these limits. The concept isn't to change animals into different beings through either training or energy work, but to support them to their full expression. If you want a lap dog, be aware of the breed characteristics of the parents. Small, cute dogs aren't necessarily cuddlers. Exotic cat breeds aren't all couch potatoes.

ENVIRONMENTAL, MEDICAL, OR EMOTIONAL?

When an Australian Shepherd suddenly begins chewing on his legs, the woodwork and furniture, consider the environment first, what changed? No amount of energy work or veterinary intervention can make up for lack of exercise and lack of stimulation. However, if there is an emotional change in the household—divorce, death or anger—energy work can help the animal resolve issues of grief and loss. The animal taking on our issues, physical or mental, does not help us and distresses the animal.

When a previously litter-box consistent cat starts peeing in unlikely places, the first thing to do is to schedule an appointment with a veterinarian! Max, who would have preferred to limit the household to one cat, began peeing on top of the vented, covered litter box and on a new stove a year after the caregiver adopted a second cat. The problem wasn't jealousy as the caregiver suspected; it was a bladder infection. The litter box vent and metal grates over the stove's burners gave Georgie something to hang on to for leverage. Peeing with a bladder infection is difficult and painful.

EMOTIONAL HEALING FOR ANIMALS

If your animal is healthy and her environmental needs for food, exercise, companionship, and stimulation are met, but she is chronically anxious, hyperalert, or depressed, treatment by an energy worker could help. Bay, a beautiful gelding with a loving home, consistently held his head high as if he were about to flee or fight. The caregiver suspected Bay had been tied and left to struggle, pull and strain in panic until he finally surrendered in exhaustion and defeat. Even though Bay could now be tied, he was skittish and always wary. He was hypervigilant; his neck always showed strain. One energy session cleared the tension in his neck and allowed him to relax. A second session released the trauma from his past and allowed him to have a trusting relationship with humans and develop a deep bond with his caregiver.

Major, a six-year-old retired racing greyhound, trembled and hid whenever there was a loud noise. Fourth of July, storms, and military firing range exercises filled him with anxiety. His caregiver, Lesa wrote:

> We took Major for one session of Healing Touch for his thunder fear. We live near Ft. Lewis and right after the Fourth of July, between the neighbors and the military, Major spent more time in his Thundershirt® than out of it. Major is pretty laid back usually, but he can get very worked up with the pacing and panting. If we don't get the shirt on and a Benadryl in time, he can go into an episode of this for over an hour or more. Wanda gave us some tips of different things to try to redirect his attitude toward the noises during his energy session.

> I can honestly say we haven't had an episode like that since our visit and we're not doing a whole lot of anything different with him. We can now get him to come down to the kitchen so we can do what we call the "yea game," giving a treat and saying "yea" whenever there's a thunder or boom. Before the session with Wanda, Major would rush upstairs to the hallway and shudder with fear, pant uncontrollably, and be completely inconsolable until he went to sleep. We haven't had that kind of reaction since our session.

THE ANIMALS IN YOUR LIFE

Nat Herzog, an anthrozoologist, objectively looks at issues such as the "Importance of Being Cute," "The Comparative Cruelty of Cockfights and Happy Meals," and "The Moral Status of Mice" in his book, *Some we Love, Some we Hate, Some we Eat*. He points out the tremendous inconsistencies in our culture. He challenges our ideas on the role of animals in our lives in the chapter titled "The Cats in Our Houses, the Cows on Our Plates: Are We All Hypocrites?"

Herzog points out that only in America do large groups of people treat their animals as children or see them as oracles. He discusses the difficulty of a "no-kill" philosophy—how far does it extend? To fleas? To mosquitoes? Is the value of an animal, any animal's, life equal to the value of a human's life? Where is the line? How do we know? How do we live with these contradictions in our lives? If you are passionate about animals and want to challenge your beliefs, read his book.

When our animal is ailing, we don't care about the broader philosophical implications of spending hundreds or thousands of dollars on medical care for our beloved companion when many people cannot get basic medical care. Our relationship with our animals is full of contradictions as is our relationship with the other complex issues of our society. Those who have the opportunity and financial ability to provide healthcare for their animals will continue to do so. Cleaning our dinner plate does not feed a child in another country. Likewise, choosing not to treat an animal does not provide medical care to a homeless person. Everyone and everything is interrelated and interconnected. We do our best with what we have and where we are in life. A decision we make today may not be the decision we make tomorrow.

DO ANIMALS REFLECT HUMAN ISSUES?

Many human clients with health issues are concerned that their animals are sick or anxious because they are sick. If a woman has back pain and her dog has weakened hindquarters, she may wonder if her beloved animal is taking on her symptoms in an effort to heal her or share her burden. A deeply grieving man notices the cat seems depressed too. An achy, stiff caregiver notices her horse appears to feel the same way. People, already discouraged by their health or life circumstances, often add guilt to their burdens—they've made their animals sick!

Carol Komitor teaches that animals' biofields are ten times their body size. When you sit next to your 65-pound Labrador, you are sitting inside the dog's biofield. Animals are much more aware of humans than we are of them. In the wild, animals rely on their ability to sense other animals for survival: eat or be eaten. When animals have a working relationship with humans, they are attuned to our physical and emotional nuances, just as we are to theirs. Sometimes the beautiful spirit of our animals lifts us from the doldrums into an appreciation of the moment. Sometimes our continued doldrums result in us not responding to our animals' needs for exercise, play, or novel experiences, and their mood shifts to reflect ours.

When we have prolonged physical, mental, emotional or spiritual issues that our animals are exposed to over time, it is reasonable that our decreased well-being influences our animals. There are times when an animal's disease does seem to mirror the human's disease. These situations may truly be coincidental—many people have back pain; many animals have back pain. Sometimes there may be a synergistic relationship between the person and the animal—when one feels great, so does the other and vice versa.

Sophie, my Lhasa Apso/Maltese therapy dog, began visiting in the hospital, when she was only a year old. We visited on the first floor in the surgery waiting areas and sometimes made special visits to the Critical Care Unit. After a few visits, I noticed my sweet dog's tail began to droop and she walked more tentatively through the hallway. She seemed to be taking on the patient's health problems.

Animals need to know that humans have the ability to handle their problems, no matter how challenging they are. Our animals' role in supporting human healing is to hold their high vibration of unconditional love. Now that Sophie knows she does not need to take on human problems, her tail is up and she walks confidently down the halls and into people's arms, loving and accepting them unconditionally. Patients are pulled into the present. In that moment, there is only the patient and the dog. All else fades.

If you feel your beloved animal is taking on your problems and literally feeling your pain, it is your responsibility to change this. Tell your animal friend that you are capable of handling your issues, and the animal's only responsibility is to do what he/she naturally does—love unconditionally.

Commit to healing yourself. Do whatever is needed to repair your mental, emotional, physical, and spiritual health—see a physician, a counselor, a naturopath, an energy healer. If you are making your animal sick, do something different, if not for yourself, then for your beloved companion. You may not be cured, but you can be healed.

ANIMALS AS PHYSICAL HEALERS

A relatively new concept in living with animals is that our animals are our healers. You may have a special animal in your life that was with you during a stressful time. If you had been alone, you might have slowly deteriorated. However, because you had this dear animal who needed feeding and walking, and who nestled close to you at night, or waited for you every morning, you made the effort day after day to pull yourself out of bed and out of the house until eventually, it was more of a joy than an effort to greet your animal friend. Did your animal help you heal? Absolutely.

We know that therapy dogs help lower blood pressure; alert dogs warn people of seizures; service dogs allow people to be more independent. However, when people talk about animals sent to them to be their healer, they are not talking about a dog that gets them outside for more exercise, or birds that bring a smile with their song. People are talking about emotional support—unconditional love, intuitive understanding and "being there" for them. If you believe your beloved animal is your healer, you are right. If you don't believe the animal is your healer, you are also right (but you might be wrong!).

People share their home with many animals over their lifetime, but there is often one animal that is more special than the others. That one animal has a closer bond to you, even though the animal is the same breed, color, and size as other animals that have shared your life. People who love animals often have a deeply felt, heart-centered connection with one or two special animals over decades. These animals certainly do support our healing and well-being. However, it is our job to heal ourselves—not our animal's job, our therapist's job or our doctor's job.

Some animals, without special training, sense illness and try to alleviate it. The *Mirror News*, Aug. 15, 2013, reported Fiona Cole's experience with her cocker spaniel, Daisy, who at first pawed her left breast, then escalated to head butting over a four-week period. When Fiona had her bruised breast examined, her doctor found a cancerous lump. I watched my therapy dog Zelda lay her head gently against the site of a friend's recent mastectomy. Her behavior was unprompted and untrained. She consistently sought out people who were ill and comforted them by molding her body against theirs.

ARE WE OUR ANIMALS' HEALERS?

We are certainly our animals' caregivers; sometimes we are also their healers. The healing we do for animals is often an attempt to change the impression they got of humans in their last living situation. We strive to give the animals a different view of humans; to let them know that as a species, we can be kind, gentle, loving, generous, fun, helpful, loyal, and all those things the humans they knew before were not. In helping these animals, we help ourselves become more patient, giving, tolerant, and unconditionally loving than we thought possible. Energy work helps people and animals overcome the emotional scars of past abuse, neglect, and suffering through releasing trauma, restoring trust and repairing the energy system.

For reflection

1. Would you consider energy therapy for your animal's emotional, physical, mental, and/or behavioral issues?

_____

_____

_____

_____

2. What are you willing to do for yourself if your issues negatively affect your animals?

_____

_____

_____

_____

3. What is the role of people and animals in your physical, emotional, mental, and spiritual healing?

_____

_____

_____

_____

_____

4. In what ways do you influence the healing of people and animals in your life?

_____

_____

_____

_____

Chapter Six
IMPACTING THE TOTAL SELF

Because energy work affects the total system—mental, physical, emotional, and spiritual—there are often unanticipated benefits from the work. Shandra came for energy work at the recommendation of her counselor. She was struggling to resolve emotionally painful issues. Her health history included double breast surgery seven years earlier. When she sat up after her initial session, the first thing she said was, "The pain is gone." Shandra was referring to a persistent pain in her right breast that was there since the initial surgery. She consulted with her doctor about the pain, but the doctor could not find a reason for it or a way to alleviate it. Shandra lived with the pain for seven years. It was such a part of her life she didn't mention it during the intake. The process of clearing and balancing her energetic system unexpectedly resolved the pain.

UNEXPLAINED SENSATIONS

In 2005, I experienced a series of falls. I fell hard, three times. The first time, I was going down the stairs at a restaurant. The second time, I fell in front of a store. My third fall happened walking with friends on a wide, level trail. This time I went to the doctor for x-rays of the hand I used to try to catch myself. The x-rays showed a tiny bone fragment floating near the knuckle of my left index finger. The doctor said if the fragment moved in the next few days, I would need surgery to pin it to the bone.

That evening, I attended Elly's monthly Healing Touch practice group, still shaken from the fall. I wondered if something larger was going on—Multiple Sclerosis, some other devastating, unnamed illness? The practitioners formed groups around the treatment tables for healing exchanges. We were a mixed bunch; some, like me, were new to Healing Touch. Others were experienced practitioners expert in more than one modality. Group members rotated between being the practitioner and the client. Treatments were twenty minutes or less to allow everyone to give and receive a mini-treatment.

In my group, I was the first to receive. I closed my eyes and the two practitioners began a Healing Touch protocol. I could feel their hands on each side of my body as they completed a Chakra Connection. During the treatment, someone joined the group and held my ankles down to the table so heavily that I was physically uncomfortable. As I lay there, I debated opening my eyes and telling the person to lighten the pressure. I assumed whoever it was must be new and didn't know to use a gentle touch.

After much internal debate, I decided not to interrupt the treatment, but wait to say something afterwards. More internal dialog, and I decided not to say anything about the heavy touch. It wasn't up to me to criticize or correct others. However, the weight on my ankles was so uncomfortable I couldn't relax. Eventually I decided I would let it go and thank the person when the treatment was complete. After all, the positive intention to assist was more important.

When I opened my eyes, only the two original practitioners were present. I asked where the third person was. I wanted to say thank you. They told me only the two of them had been present, but they recommended I thank the other "person." This was the first time I had the experience of feeling another's "hands" on my body during a session.

When my hand was x-rayed a few days later, the bone fragment remained in place. Surgery was unnecessary. My instructor Bernie Clarke asked me to write up this experience as a testimonial for the Healing Touch Program. I hesitated. Did the treatment really prevent the fragment from moving? As I considered writing about the incident, I realized over the months I'd participated in the practice group, I'd stopped taking the muscle relaxant, anti-inflammatory, and hormones I took for years. I didn't stop intentionally; I just forgot to take them so often I never refilled the prescriptions.

Experiences of pressure on the body, and other unexplained sensations during energetic treatments, occur regularly. People who feel pressure where the practitioner's hands are not, interpret the event through their belief framework. Some people say angels placed their hands on them; others just say they thought my hands were at their head, but they felt me at their feet. Others avoid attributing physical qualities and refer only to pressure at various points on their body. Naming the source is not important. Awareness of the sensations in and around your body during a treatment and speculating on what they mean is interesting. Defining their origin is not important.

Today, I take no prescription medications. Is this due to my continued involvement in energy work, good genetics, something else, or a combination of the above? This is precisely the difficulty with research into energy medicine, with anecdotal reports and even with personal experience. There are so many confounding factors that it is unclear which intervention is responsible for what outcome, which brings us back to the haystack theory of healing.

I have witnessed, heard, and read many stories of miraculous healings with energy work. Miraculous healing also occurs with traditional Western and Eastern medicine. The patient is not expected to overcome the disease or injury, but does! Often patients attribute their healing to the last intervention they had. However, healing and personal growth occur because of everything we bring to the process, all the avenues we try, and every intervention we undertake.

No two people are the same, even though their circumstances may be similar. Even though our lives run parallel to another's due to shared activities and interests, we do not have the same experiences. There may be commonalities—both people experienced a Traumatic Brain Injury; both people lost their dearly beloved to an early death; both people are alcoholics—but one person's experience is not the same as the other's experience. Our journey and our healing is unique.

WHO HEALS? ANGELS OR THE DEVIL?

When I asked a colleague after the Healing Touch Level 4 course if she had started the 100 required sessions for certification, she said she stopped doing energy work. Her church was against it. I was flabbergasted. I grew up attending a fundamentalist church that believed in hands on healing. Although I left my childhood church long ago, I was shocked that anyone would think such beautiful, nurturing work was evil.

An Internet search quickly found a site deploring the use of Healing Touch as the Devil's work. Another site declared that the Catholic Church was against Reiki, saying it was based on superstition. I called my mentor, Sherri Cote, for her opinion.

She said, "Only God heals." For me, that was enough. Hands on healing is deeply rooted in Christian culture and in many other cultures. Although I do not believe in God the same way I did as a child, it seems obvious that good only comes from good.

IS A BELIEF IN GOD NECESSARY TO HEALING?

Of the modalities I am familiar with, only the Institute of Spiritual Healing and Aromatherapy (ISHA) espouses a particular religious belief system. ISHA is rooted in the Christian tradition of hands on healing and anointing with oils. Linda Smith, the founder, originally worked with Janet Mentgen, the founder of Healing Touch. Mentgen's goal was for Healing Touch to be accepted in hospitals and available to patients as a matter of course. Smith wanted to revive the traditions of the church. Mentgen and Smith developed their programs from a common base that diverged to reflect their personal visions.

Lack of connection to a religion does not imply that energy healing practitioners are not spiritual. Healers will tell you they facilitate healings; they are not responsible for them. Healers are as diverse as the general population in their beliefs about angels, beings, and entities. Many healers work with guides or other non-physical beings. If practitioners reference a higher being, they generally do so in the broadest of terms— Source of all that is, God of your understanding—in order to acknowledge that a power greater than themselves is doing the healing. This leaves clients free to see the healing within the context of their beliefs. Practitioners and clients do not need to believe in any particular religion or spiritual hierarchy. Many modalities recommend grounding (energetically connecting to the center of the earth), centering (bringing one's attention to the present moment), and focusing (narrowing thoughts to the task), prior to a session.

When I came to this work, I had no belief in angelic healings, guides, power animals, or any of the myriad of other beings populating the lives of some people. However, when I began offering sessions, I saw and heard things that I didn't believe in my treatment room. I thought I must be just imagining Archangel Michael holding and comforting clients. At times, I saw and heard people from my clients' lives apologizing, explaining, comforting.   When I shared words from these scenes, my clients confirmed their authenticity. My mentor assured me these experiences were blessings, not signs of an overactive imagination.

My personal concept of the spiritual world is ever evolving. I am satisfied with being open to phenomena as I perceive them without attaching rightness or wrongness. What I see is true for me; that doesn't mean it's true for you. Your experiences in life and on a treatment table are yours. Your perception of the session is the most important. What a practitioner experiences may or may not ring true for you. Take what resonates with you and leave the rest.

PEOPLE ARE ROSES, NOT ONIONS

Professionals often reference the onion metaphor when talking about emotional healing. They say, "It's like peeling an onion, one layer at a time." Many people have an unspoken fear that when their onion is completely peeled, a dark, unlovable part of them will be revealed at the core. A rejected person may feel, "This person who loved me and knew me more intimately than anyone in my life has ever known me discovered what I have always known: that at my core, I am unlovable. That's why I'm alone."

People are roses, not onions. The layers are not peeling away; rather the petals are unfurling. At the core is a golden center filled with love and light. We are raised by parents, influenced by teachers, and rejected by lovers who did not/could not see our golden core. As children, we accepted the view of these influential people in our lives as true. Energy healers see the light in you, honor it, and help you discover it for yourself.

For Reflection

1. Who do you believe heals?

_____

_____

_____

_____

2. What does the statement "all healing is self-healing" mean to you?

_____

_____

_____

_____

3. Have you experienced unexplainable phenomena?

_____

_____

_____

_____

Chapter Seven
HEALING INTO DEATH

Bernie Siegel maintains that if we focus on curing and view death as a failure, we are "losing sight of ways to help them [patients] in their transition through death." He advises both healthy and ill people to live as if they were going to die tonight. If we do this, we will live fully, with no regrets.

HEALING, NOT CURING

Healing and curing are not the same. Being cured means the physical, mental, emotional or spiritual problem is completely removed and will not recur. Healing includes physical recovery, soothing childhood wounds, releasing bullying work situations, letting go of destructive love relationships, as well as finding peace with existing conditions. Energy practitioners do not profess to cure people or animals. They facilitate healing. A young man with a life-threatening illness told me that during his Healing Touch session, a wonderful childhood memory came to him at every hand placement. I don't know if he lived or died that year, but his experience was a healing.

People who want to die often don't, and those who want to live don't. My friend Maria had cancer for a very long time. She went through agonizing treatments that left her exhausted and in pain. She worked in an office throughout the long years of treatment. Sometimes the cancer was in remission, sometimes not. Many times, she thought she was going to die. Many times, she wished she would. But she didn't. She fell in love. When she fell in love and wanted to live, she died. She died happy, cradled in the love of the universe and the love of her family and friends. For the last few months of her life, she lived fully; she loved fully. In the peace and joy of love, she died.

Many elderly people are waiting to die; but don't. Elizabeth has been waiting to die for some years now. She has outlived her husband, her siblings, and her peers. She has a comfortable home, a loving family, and wonderful care. She walks with a walker, has some aches and pains, and has lost much of her memory and the ability to do activities she once enjoyed. If asked if she is happy, she says no. If asked if she'd rather be dead, she says yes. But she doesn't die; she lives. I wonder if she saw the blessings in her surroundings and joy in the details of each day, if she might die. Even if she didn't die, she would be happier. Perhaps when we reach peace with life as it is, death takes us.

Healing into death is accepting death as inevitable and life as a gift. In the time we have, whether moments or years, do we value life? Do we use our breath to love and appreciate this world and those around us? Or do we curse our body's resiliency and determination to go on?

CHOOSING DEATH

Amanda's husband died three years before I met her. She was financially secure, had a chronic, progressive, potentially debilitating disease and one close relative. She cried every morning as she looked at her husband's photo across from her at the breakfast table. When doctors told her she probably had lung cancer, she was grateful. She opted not to have a biopsy to confirm the diagnosis and declined treatment. She stopped her medications, took to her bed, and died within weeks.

I wanted her to choose life; she refused. She wanted me to help her die; I refused. I did go to her home every few days to provide Healing Touch. The energy therapy soothed her, made her more comfortable, and perhaps helped her in other ways. She assured me choosing death was the right choice. She was at peace when she died.

My partner, Lloyd, was misdiagnosed with lung cancer. Complications from the lung resection to remove the cancer followed by a second surgery left him respirator dependent. He entered the hospital expecting to be released in five days, spend six weeks recovering at home, and then return to his usual activities. Despite the efforts of his doctors, the operation and complications left him with insufficient lung capacity to fill his body's oxygen needs.

During the five and a half months Lloyd was in the hospital, his children spent time with him every week. When he was well enough and not sedated, we sorted through our pictures that we'd tossed in drawers over the years. We relived those happy days as I placed the photos in albums. When Lloyd didn't feel well enough for a project, we were together and it was enough. He told me he had lived a good life. He said dying was harder on the living than the dying. He called his children together and made clear his wishes that the respirator be turned off and he be allowed to die. And so it happened. He died peacefully, grateful to pass on to that other world. He healed into death. It took much longer for me to heal back into life.

Last year, I received a midnight call from a stranger. Janice's mother was in the hospital unexpectedly with no hope of surviving. She found my number on the Healing Touch Program's website and took the chance of calling even though it was the middle of the night. I live close to the hospital, so I dressed quickly and went over. When I arrived, Janice's mother was struggling to breathe; fighting, and gasping for air despite the oxygen delivered through a nasal cannula. I did a full treatment for her, then a mini-treatment for Janice. Her mother ceased her struggle and remained calm until dying peacefully with Janice at her side a few days later. The energy work, the caring medical intervention, and her daughter's love supported her peaceful passing.

MAKING A PERSONAL CHOICE

"How Doctors Die: It's Not Like the Rest of Us, But it Should Be," according to Ken Murray. He says doctors don't die like the rest of us; they die with much less intervention when faced with life-ending conditions. He describes doctors' frustration with "futile care" that might increase the quantity of a person's life by a small amount, but decreases the quality of life immensely. When my father's doctor described the treatment options for his cancer, I asked what the possibility was for a cure. The doctor said he wasn't talking about a cure, but life extension. When I asked for how long, he said it could be as much as three months. After a few rounds of challenging chemotherapy, my father stopped all treatment. He died as he chose at age 63.

When it is time to make end of life decisions for me, I want to make them. I want to fully understand the treatment possibilities, their positives and negatives, and make my choice to have them or not. I wish everyone this same opportunity. In the best of circumstances, you have already communicated your wishes through a Living Will and verbally to your Medical Power of Attorney (you have one, right?).

More often than you might think, people are thrust into life and death situations that leave them unable to speak for themselves. Perhaps the individual is under sedation, has an emergency tracheotomy, is in a coma, or has had a stroke and suddenly cannot speak or write. It seems obvious that our Advanced Directives will be followed. However, there is no guarantee. Your Medical Power of Attorney makes choices based on his/her understanding of your wishes, the situation, the feelings of family members and the treatment options. I implore you, take the few minutes required to formalize your end of life wishes in writing and make them known to your family. At the same time, make arrangements for your animals in case of your unexpected inability to care for them.

Whether you want to be maintained on life support or not, it is important for those in charge of your care to know your desires so they can implement your wishes without guilt. It is equally important that your Medical Power of Attorney is in agreement and supports your decisions. Occasions do occur when the trusted Medical Power of Attorney decides to go against the expressed wishes of the dying. You want the person with power over your life or death to use informed judgment when you cannot speak for yourself and you want them to honor your requests.

THE FINAL DECISION FOR YOUR BELOVED ANIMAL

We seldom have to make a life or death choice for our loved ones or ourselves, but such a choice is common for those who live with animals. Many of us would prefer for our dear animals die peacefully and naturally at home by our side. My experience is that this seldom happens. Even if the death is natural and occurs at home, it is seldom the death we envisioned. Your beloved animal may die behind your chair while you are cooking dinner or hide outside in the shrubbery to die alone or die during a seizure.

My animals have died at home and with veterinarian help. Ezra, my Devon Rex companion cat, died without warning while I was visiting Lloyd at the hospital. Ebenezer, my Cornish Rex, died a few months later. I was at home and knew the end was near. He did not appear to be in pain or terribly uncomfortable. I tried to hold him, but he struggled against me. I laid him down near the heater, thinking the warmth would feel good. He crawled away, dying in mid-movement.

There are no old animals in the wild. Prey animals are struck down when they weaken, dying swiftly, supporting the ever-renewing cycle of life. Predators experience the same fate as they age. Our feeble and ill animals live in protected environments with water, food, medications, and loving care. Their bodies' purpose is to survive, and survive they do even though they may be emaciated by disease and unable to eat or stand. When an animal's caregivers tell me they want a few more months with their beloved animal, they do not mean they want more months of pain and suffering. They want more time with their animal friend happy and comfortable, even if physically impaired.

Sometimes we can have months or years with our aging or fragile animals; oftentimes we cannot. Carol Komitor, founder of Healing Touch for Animals, maintains our final responsibility is to release our animals from their suffering and let them die peacefully. If this is through veterinary intervention, so be it.

The decision of when to put an animal down is difficult and emotional. In *Love, Miracles, and Animal Healing*, Schoen relates a haunting experience with end-of-life for an ill English setter. The setter's caregivers took her to Schoen for euthanization. After examining the dog, he assured them it was possible her life could be saved. Her caregivers consulted with each other and chose euthanasia. Despite the doctor's insistence he could save their dog, the couple felt strongly the dog was telling them she wanted to die. Euthanizing the setter haunted Dr. Shoen for years afterwards.

If I had not had a similar experience, I might judge these people harshly. When my beloved Miniature Schnauzer Zelda became deathly ill one morning, I too heard her saying, "I want to die." I carried her to an emergency appointment with her veterinarian. In the examination room, the assistant went through the routine questions, Did I want cremation? Group or individual? Did I want a paw print? Tears ran down my cheeks as I signed the final papers. When Zelda's veterinarian, Dr. Molitor, came into the room, he gently examined her.

Because I always bring a stool sample with me whenever one of our dogs sees the veterinarian, my partner John picked up Zelda's stool that morning and handed it to me as I left. Since I had the sample, Dr. Molitor said he would check it. While he was gone, I told Zelda how much I loved her and that I understood it was time for her to leave. When Dr. Molitor returned, he told me Zelda had a bacterial infection and prescribed antibiotics plus an additional medication to treat her pre-existing heart condition. With the help of the antibiotics, Zelda quickly recovered. Her original health problems remained, but she no longer wanted to die. She enjoyed life for some months longer. It was only in that moment of pain and misery that she wanted to die; if she could feel better, she wanted to live!

We all want to do what is best for our loved ones—human and animal—but our resolve can be clouded by our desire to keep those we love present in the flesh. I treated a cat that was half her healthy weight. She'd had an unsuccessful operation for cancer and was not eating. The caregiver pleaded, "If we could just have another month." But she didn't mean another month of emaciation, weakness, pain and weight loss; she meant a month of health and vibrancy, which was not possible.

Many years ago, my work colleague and friend sat with her head resting in her arms on the table in the break room saying, "I just want to die." She was undergoing aggressive therapy for breast cancer. My friend did not die; she lived and is still alive 40 years later. She helped hundreds of people through her work. After retirement she continued to contribute to her community and care for her neighbors. So many people would have lost so much if she had died early.

Some circumstances are so painful, so difficult, and so wearing that people and animals lose their zest for life. However, when the crisis is over and the quality of life improves, they treasure life and its gifts, even if their physical capacities remain diminished. They continue to make a positive difference despite their limitations. Because recovery may be a possibility, getting medical counsel before making the irreversible decision to end another being's life can give you peace with your final decision.

EUTHANASIA – ZELDA'S STORY

My Miniature Schnauzer Zelda came to Lloyd and me as a puppy in 2000. From the beginning, she was calm, loving, and sensitive to the aches and pains of others. She quickly learned basic obedience and to be comfortable in stores and with a wide variety of people. When she was four, I completed the three-month training to volunteer with her at the Providence Hospital in Olympia. We took the Delta Pet Partners® Skills and Aptitude test and passed on our first attempt.

We volunteered on Inpatient Rehabilitation for six years. If patients were in deep distress, Zelda would lie next them and mold her body to theirs. Sometimes patients held her tightly. Sometimes they cried. Sometimes they whispered softly to her. The patients and staff were deeply appreciative of her presence. Other times, Zelda would sit on the lap of a patient having a particularly difficult time and lay her head on the person's heart, providing deep, silent comfort.

As Zelda aged, I knew she could not continue her work as a therapy dog for many more years. With Zelda's help, I trained another puppy, Sophie, a Lhasa Apso/Maltese cross, as a therapy dog. Sophie and I became a Delta Therapy Team when she was one year old. In 2010, Zelda retired from therapy work.

Two years later, her health faltered. I dreaded her death. Zelda was my last connection to my life with Lloyd. I had sold our home, vehicles, even most of our furniture and started over, but I didn't want to lose her too. I experienced reverberations from Lloyd's loss every time I thought of Zelda dying. I cried whenever I thought of her inevitable demise, even though it was months away.

Zelda had arthritis, an enlarged liver, a painful spine, and congestive heart failure. She was on two heart medications, pain medication and muscle relaxants. Her breathing was shallow. When she became excited or over-exerted, she fainted from lack of oxygen to her brain. Still, she ate, went on walks, and enjoyed life. However, her body sagged away from her backbone. She slept on her side, belly distended, legs stretched out to breathe more easily.

On her last night, Zelda refused all medications although she seemed painful. She slept without moving where I placed her at the end of the bed. During the night, I dreamed Zelda was sitting on the bank of a river as I sped away in a boat. I shouted, "I can't leave her" and woke up with a start. I checked Zelda to see if she was still alive. I carried her downstairs and offered her medication and food. Again she refused. I knew she was done. I called the emergency veterinarian.

The Vet Tech showed us into a small, dimly lit room furnished like a living room. Zelda received a shot to make her sleepy, then the life-ending dose of anesthetic. She died instantly. The moment her breath stopped, I felt release and flight, like a fluttering. She was not dead, but released, as Lloyd was released. I was released too—released from worry, from sadness, from fear. I saw Zelda and Lloyd happy together. Our connection didn't break; it strengthened.

I buried Zelda along the path of our daily walk. Sophie came and sniffed at the open grave, then stretched up toward me, balancing on her back feet. I leaned over and she licked the tears on my cheeks. I left on vacation for three days. When I returned, I wondered how I would feel coming home with Zelda gone. When I settled into my favorite chair, Sophie jumped up to lie next to me as Zelda had for the last 12 years. When I went to bed, Sophie took Zelda's place next to me. I knew Zelda's mission was complete. She had passed her healing torch and special place in my life to Sophie. Zelda's place was with Lloyd. She was at peace and so was I, though I still sometimes miss her physical presence.

EUTHANASIA – TAIKO'S STORY

I met Taiko, a 14-year-old Shiba Inu, in his home after a local veterinarian referred Karen to me. Taiko had renal failure and for the last three days, had refused food. A Healing Touch session was a last ditch effort to see if he would resume eating and live happily a little longer. Five days after the treatment, Karen called and left a thank you message on my phone. She said it took a few days, but Taiko was eating and appeared just fine.

Two months later, Karen called me at 8:07 a.m. with tears in her voice; today was going to be the last day of her wonderful Shiba Inu's life. She wanted Taiko to have a soothing energy treatment before he was euthanized at home. Taiko had been slow to wake that morning. During the night, he lost bladder and bowel control. On wakening, he was barely able to walk. His right rear leg dragged with the toes folding backward.

When I arrived, Taiko was on blankets and confined to a small bathroom. He was lying down, but his head was up and he was alert. He tried to get up and walk, but his right hind leg could not take any pressure. I put my hands on the joints of his right rear leg, but he moved away from me, dragging the leg. I asked Karen for a large stuffed dog to use as a surrogate. As I worked, Taiko laid down about six feet away, in sight of Karen but out of my sight. During the treatment, Taiko got up and went back to his bed in the bathroom. When Karen checked on him, he was semi-curled up, something he hadn't been able to do for some time.

As I finished treating the front legs, I felt Taiko's energy surge through him. With my hands still on the surrogate, Taiko got up and came into the main room walking on all four legs! He stood between Karen and me and shook himself. Even his tail, which had been immobile for the past year, moved a little.

We were amazed! Taiko walked around as if nothing unusual had happened. Karen called the mobile vet and cancelled Taiko's appointment. Taiko escorted me to the door and enjoyed some long body strokes before I left. He looked fit and ready for the day. Instead of seeing Taiko for the last time, I saw a miracle.

When Karen called three days later to say Taiko's leg wasn't working again, I thought perhaps he had made one last great effort for his family the last time I saw him and the end of life was near. However, when I arrived, Taiko was walking on all four legs again! I did another surrogate treatment with Taiko in the house, but not nearby. Karen emailed me a few days later to let me know "Taiko has done very well all weekend, including taking a little walk in the snow. He has always loved snow! He has been stable outside in the backyard and walking well." Taiko lived happy and healthy many months more.

EUTHANASIA – HANNAH'S STORY

It would be lovely if every person and animal experienced an amazing recovery to full health, but energy therapy is about healing, not curing. Hannah was a beautiful, 14-year-old Siberian Husky who stopped eating. Her original coloring had lightened to a warm white. Hannah had Cushing's disease. Even so, she appeared too vital to be so close to death. Hannah allowed me to place my hands on her and treat her on her comfortable, cushioned mat. She relaxed into the treatment. I was tickled to see Hannah's face after the session—I swear she smiled! After the session, she stood up and accepted treats from her devoted caregiver.

The treatment revived Hannah so she could continue to take brief walks. She even regained bladder control. I treated Hannah a few more times before I got the final call. Hannah had never really begun eating again. She accepted treats throughout the day, but it was clear her health was declining. When Hannah could hardly lift her body, her caregiver made the final, difficult, loving decision to let Hannah go. I met them at the veterinary office.

Hannah was lying on the examination room floor when I arrived, the IV already placed. I did one last treatment and Hannah got up! She wanted to go outside! We quickly gathered the leash and IV bag and walked her out the side door into the cold night air. Given a choice, Hannah would have continued walking into the starry night, as I imagine her ancestors would have walked toward their death. However, we didn't know if we would be able to carry Hannah back to the clinic if she collapsed, so we turned around.

When we returned to the examination room, the veterinarian showed Hannah's latest x-ray. Hannah had a tumor that crowded her stomach to the point there was no room for food and digestion. While we talked, Hannah walked around the room with a happy smile on her face. When the veterinarian gave the final injection, Hannah slid into the afterlife gently and quickly. We cried, but Hannah was content. She is deeply missed. Her wonderful presence will always be remembered and honored.

For Reflection

1. How can a person or animal heal into death?

_____

_____

_____

2. What is your experience with decisions to have your animals euthanized?

_____

_____

_____

3. What is your experience with allowing animals to die naturally?

_____

_____

_____

4. How do you feel about making the decision or implementing another person's decision to end life?

_____

_____

_____

_____

5. What do you want for yourself at end of life?

_____

_____

_____

_____

Section Three:

TAKING ACTION

Insofar as it can change our participation in disease, every [healing] system is capable of working.

--Deepak Chopra, *Quantum Healing: Exploring the Frontiers of Mind/Body Medicine.*

Chapter Eight
CHOOSING A PRACTITIONER

Practitioners are unique as you are unique. Choose someone whose style, manner, and approach feels comfortable to you. Most people and animals experience an immediate, positive benefit from a single session. Three to five sessions often yield exponential results.

Once you've decided to have energy therapy for yourself, your family, or your animals, how do you find the right practitioner? Recommendations from professionals are a good place to start—your doctor, naturopath, or veterinarian—however, they may not know any energy practitioners. Medical professionals may also be concerned that their reputation will suffer if they recommend complementary treatments. They may also be constrained by a network referral system. Recommendations from your friends can be useful if their reasons for seeking complementary treatment are similar to yours.

FINDING A LOCAL PRACTITIONER

Locating a geographically convenient practitioner can be challenging. The telephone book yellow pages are no longer up to date, authoritative guides to businesses in your area. Energy healers seldom advertise through this medium due to the cost, the number of directory publishers, and the low return on their investment. Directories of alternative and complementary resources may be available in your community on the Internet or occasionally in print. These directories list some of the healers in your community, but are limited to practitioners who have paid a fee to the publishing organization.

Just as people have difficulty locating energy workers, practitioners have difficulty finding new clients. Some practitioners volunteer or rent booths at Health Fairs or offer low cost or no cost educational talks to the public. Some practitioners teach classes. However, with the exception of Reiki, becoming a certified instructor in any modality is a demanding, time consuming, and costly process. Some modalities limit the number of instructors. Many practitioners are not interested in teaching; they prefer facilitating the healing of their clients.

A good option for locating practitioners is to visit energy modality websites and search the Practitioner Directory. Healing Touch Program, Reconnective Healing, Matrix Energetics, Healing Touch for Animals and other modalities have directories on their site. Practitioners must complete the minimum course requirements and pay a fee for their directory listing. Sometimes practitioners pay an additional fee to have their photo and website included. Many practitioners study multiple modalities and do not pay for listings in every modality. Check practitioner websites to find the range of services they provide.

Practitioners' websites give their background, including training, credentials, and client testimonials. Use the email address or phone number provided to contact the practitioner and ask questions. Most practitioners give free consultations. You can also search for practitioners by modality on Facebook and through Linked In and similar professional networks.

GOVERNMENT OVERSIGHT

States vary in their oversight of complementary modalities and licensing requirements. In general, practitioners who manipulate the body, such as massage therapists and chiropractors must be licensed by the state where they practice. Since energy practitioners do not manipulate body tissue or joints, most states do not require a license to practice, provide oversight of the workers, or set minimum training requirements.

Many modalities have a certification procedure for practitioners as well as a code of ethics and scope of practice practitioners agree to follow. If clients have complaints or concerns, they contact the modality's governing body. An ethics board investigates the complaint or responds to the concern. If the complaint is found valid, the practitioner's credentials are revoked.

CHOOSING A PRACTITIONER WITH LIMITED EXPERIENCE

Many practitioners have small businesses based on referrals and work from a home or shared office. They do not have a website or directory listings. These practitioners may be new to the work or just starting a formal energy healing business after retiring from another career. Being new to the work does not mean the practitioners are ineffective; it means they have less experience and probably charge less. You can expect price ranges similar to those for massage in your community. Well-known practitioners often charge more.

When I began my energy healing practice, I provided up to five free sessions. My clients came to me by referral only. Due to my inexperience, I often listened too much or talked too much and the session extended beyond the allotted appointment time. I struggled with being neutral about the outcome. I wanted my clients to heal the way they wanted to heal! I had difficulty remaining within my scope of practice; it was easy and tempting to give advice. My clients were my teachers as much as my coursework had been. The energy flowed and together we experienced healings.

Ariel, a Reconnective Healing Practitioner, posted his experience with his dad on the Reconnection website. His father had breathing problems throughout his life, including the removal of a lung when he was a teenager. His dad tried everything, but nothing alleviated the problem. Ariel enrolled in Reconnective Healing classes with the intent of helping his father. The first session Ariel did for his dad had a profound effect. Ariel wrote, "He [Dad] no longer needs to constantly cough and spit out mucus. When he lies down in bed, mucus no longer runs up his chest and so he can finally actually sleep through the night without waking up coughing. I no longer have to experience what it's like to live a life where it constantly sounds like my dad is dying."

An inexperienced practitioner can facilitate amazing results. Shortly after taking Healing Touch Program Level 1, Joanie wrote about her experience treating a two-year old. Her friend's toddler had a life threatening condition that required surgery. She asked Joanie to do energy healing while the child was still in the hospital. Joanie visited the toddler twice. She conscientiously followed the Healing Touch protocol of pre-assessment, treatment based on the assessment, and post assessment. The toddler's parents reported the best nights of sleep the little girl had in the hospital were after the energy sessions. She recovered from the surgery and returned home with her grateful parents. Did the energy sessions make the difference and stem the tide of illness? We will never know. Did they contribute to the child's recovery and the parents' peace of mind? Yes.

Nancy Rebecca, www.intuitivemind.org, said it so well. "Even at this beginning level, profound things can happen because we are profound beings." The biggest difference between when I first began working as an energy healer and now is that giving and receiving the work changed me. I healed and grew—physically, emotionally, mentally, and spiritually. I meditate more. I am neutral about the outcome. I know and practice that all healing is self-healing. I have more training and offer more options to my clients. I talk less. I am less distracted by people's stories. Energy work is not talk therapy; it goes where talk cannot. The magic happens on the table.

When I started my energy healing business, I generally recommended a series of five treatments; now I recommend three sessions before re-evaluation. My first clients sat through a long explanation of my background and how I came to Healing Touch. I felt I had to explain why I thought I could do energy treatments when my doctorate and career were in education. After the first fifty sessions, I realized my clients didn't care where I'd been. They cared about the here and now.

The ability to heal ourselves and to heal others lies latent in each of us. The practitioner's career prior to entering the field of energy work is not important. Practitioners bring the knowledge they've acquired during their lifetime to their practice. Practitioners who were medical nurses prior to becoming energy healers bring this expertise to the session. If a medical background is important to you, choose a practitioner with those credentials.

CHOOSING AN EXPERIENCED PRACTITIONER

The advantage of veteran practitioners is their greater experience, additional training, and extended time self-healing. Experienced practitioners often have training in a variety of energy modalities. Advanced coursework provides practitioners a broader range of options with which to address your concerns. They have testimonials from clients and people you can call for more information about their work.

Practitioners, who have seen many clients over an extended period, are more likely to have experience with your issue or your animal's issue. They can tell you about their previous experiences and the results in a similar situation. Practitioners with high integrity will also tell you they cannot guarantee that your results will be the same or they may refer you to another practitioner they know who might better address your concern.

Some practitioners are like portals. Their clairvoyance, clairaudience, mediumship and other extrasensory perceptions allow them to see and/or hear scenes from your life or to communicate with a living or deceased person who is deeply con-nected to you. These experiences can occur unexpectedly as part of your healing session. If this occurs for you or for the healer, check the information against your knowledge. Does the information and communication resonate with what you remember or know? Take what seems plausible to you. Leave the rest. Such communications can be very comforting or pro-vide insight into a current issue in your life.

Talk to the practitioner. Share your insights and experiences during the session. If you have questions, ask them. If you have concerns, express them. The session is about you and your healing.

CHOOSE A MODALITY THAT APPEALS TO YOU

Be clear what you want from an energy session prior to sched-uling an appointment for yourself or your animal. You can have anything from deep relaxation to radical transformation. It is up to you.

You have many choices once you decide to have an energy healing session. You can choose acupuncture and have points inserted. You can choose a touch modality like Reiki or a no touch modality, such as Pranic Healing or Reconnective Healing. Other decisions to make before you select a practitio-ner include whether you want to discuss your concerns or prefer to be silent. Individual practitioners vary in the amount of history they collect from their clients. Healing Touch Program practitioners follow a medical model that includes an intake. Reconnective Healing practitioners prefer not knowing why you scheduled an appointment. Clairvoyant practitioners can see issues in your life that may be below your awareness level. You may find this intriguing and helpful. However, if you feel such readings are prying or make-believe, select a practitioner who works with the information you provide.

Choose an energy modality you respect. Perhaps Reiki appeals to you because of its long history. Healing Touch Program might resonate with you because it follows a medical model. If you want something new, then Reconnective Healing might be what you are looking for. Perhaps you are curious about Pranic Healing. Do some reading, review practitioner websites, and talk to your friends about their experiences. Ask for a half-hour complimentary consultation.

Energy medicine is about self-healing. You choose who works in your biofield and what modality you want to experience. Commit to also supporting your healing through music, sleep, exercise, nutrition, play, work, medications if needed, massage, chiropractic, and other options. Invest at least as much effort in your healing as you ask the practitioner to invest. The practitioner isn't responsible for your healing; you are. When choosing energy therapy, you have nothing to lose except a few dollars. If what you and the practitioner are doing isn't working, do something else.

ANGELS, ENTITIES AND OTHERS

Some energy healing modalities, such as Pranic Healing and Access Consciousness, include references to God, angels, entities, life forms, and a myriad of unseen beings and energetic forces. Other modalities use more neutral terms—your higher self, universal life force, the God of your heart. Some modalities refer to clearing issues from past lives or bringing attributes from parallel lives, or future lives (such as Matrix Energetics) into the present. Other modalities only refer to the here and now. Healing Touch and Reiki reference energy flowing through (not from) the practitioner to the recipient. Reconnective Healing works with frequencies around the client and practitioner.

Whatever the stated or underlying beliefs of energetic healing systems, most modalities do not claim the practitioner is responsible for the healing. The practitioner facilitates the healing, and a force beyond the practitioner heals. Healing is between the client and the universe for the client's greatest and highest good.

You might see this philosophy as a way for the practitioner to avoid taking responsibility for the outcome of a session. If you do not feel you experienced a healing, the practitioner takes no responsibility. The converse is also true—if you experience a miraculous healing, the practitioner takes no responsibility. If you receive a healing on multiple levels that was more than you ever imagined, the practitioner doesn't claim the healing as something he/she did. With the help of a higher power or the universe or whatever you choose to name it, you self-healed.

Given this lack of a guarantee, why would you seek out energy healing? For the same reasons you go to a medical doctor. You or your animal has a condition that interferes with daily life. The problem could be anything from something minor and bothersome to a life threatening illness, but it does not yield to anything you have tried. Your doctor brings his/her expertise to the situation, makes recommendations from which you choose, and together, you proceed on a course of action. There are no guarantees in this situation either. You or your animal may or may not recover fully. The same is true of energy work.

For reflection

1. What attributes do you want in a practitioner?

_____

_____

_____

_____

_____

2. What is important to you about the modality?

_____

_____

_____

_____

_____

3. What practitioner credentials are important to you?

_____

_____

_____

_____

_____

4. What questions do you want answered before a session?

_____

_____

_____

_____

_____

Chapter Nine
CONSIDERING PRACTICAL MATTERS

Ask practitioners about confidentiality, scope of practice, and their training and experience. Established healers working with a modality that has a national presence probably use an informed consent form (which is also a disclaimer that what they do does not replace traditional medical or mental health care). They subscribe to a code of ethics and have a defined scope of practice. Informed consent gives you information about practitioners' training and the limits of their work. A code of ethics ensures the practitioner will not discuss your personal or medical history or session with anyone, including the person who referred you.

Scope of practice refers to what the practitioner's training qualifies him/her to do. Practitioners' training sets limits on what they can advise their clients. Training in clearing and balancing the biofield does not give the practitioner the expertise to consult on diet or advise you on relationship issues. Practitioners cannot offer advice on whether your horse would be better off barefoot or shod unless they have specific training in that area. Unless energy workers meet state Mental Health Counselor education and internship requirements, they cannot provide counseling. Biofield energy workers cannot diagnose illnesses or prescribe medications; this is beyond their scope of practice.

A Tarot reader once told me she saw a past life event that prevented me from living a full, happy life. She offered to do an unspecified number of additional treatments to clear this issue. Beware of fear-based marketing. Acknowledging that you have a long-term chronic issue that may take more than one treatment to resolve is realistic. Identifying a problem you were unaware of when you entered the session, then recommending extensive additional work is questionable. Ethical practitioners always leave the choice of having more sessions up to you. If what the practitioner "sees" does not resonate with you, don't take it on. The practitioner is not all knowing. You are the expert on yourself.

Be cautious about choosing practitioners based on testimonials proclaiming miraculous cures. Miracles do happen; but, like happiness, when you look hard for them, they are elusive. If you want a cure more than you want a healing, you will be disappointed.

Clients occasionally report feeling worse following an energy treatment. You may have heard this referred to as a healing crisis. Experiencing a healing crisis is not typical. If you have an adverse reaction following a session, call the practitioner! The practitioner can advise you if your experience is related to your session or independent of it. Most practitioners do distance work and can alleviate your symptoms or advise you on what you can do on your behalf to feel better. Practitioners want to know what your experience was during and after the session. Knowing this helps them improve their practice and gives them information to assist you. If you don't feel good after a session, don't wait. Call.

If you have previously had an unpleasant physical reaction to massage or energy work, tell the practitioner before the session. If you had one negative reaction, you might have another. Lucy consistently got sick following massage or energy work. When she finally sought medical attention, diagnostic tests revealed a serious infection throughout her body. Harold became nauseous during massage or energy work. Knowing how sensitive his system was, the practitioner could adjust the session length and depth. Energy work helps you feel better, not worse.

FEELING COMFORTABLE

Energy practitioners should provide a safe, confidential space where you can release emotional, physical, mental, and spiritual discomfort. You should be able to tell them whatever you choose and you shouldn't need to tell them anything at all. Healing Touch comes from a medical model. The intake form contains many questions, including a self-rating of the client's spiritual, emotional, mental, and physical well-being. I struggled with these forms and ratings. I didn't feel qualified to counsel anyone on spiritual matters, so how could I ask people to rate their spiritual well-being on a scale of 1 to 10? I finally accepted that clients' self-ratings raised issues for their reflection, not for my comment.

Do not tell the practitioner anything you don't feel comfortable sharing. Many practitioners, and some modalities, work with no information about the client. By working without advance information and with no intent, the practitioner and the client do not confine the healing to their limited intentions. Other modalities work from the intent the client expresses, tempered by the desire for the greatest good for the client, whatever that might be. Even so, you only need to divulge the specific issue you came to have treated. If you don't want to say more, don't.

If the practitioner is talking more than treating, be aware. Is the practitioner giving you advice? Trying to solve your problems? More interested in your story than your healing? An experienced practitioner talks less and listens more, asks more questions and offers fewer suggestions. Remember: the healing happens on the table. Practitioners may give insight into your situation, but every word that drops from their lips isn't God-given or the one true answer.

If you leave an energy session feeling emotionally "less than" you felt before the session, consider changing practitioners. The practitioner's role is not to judge, criticize, or advise. Ideally, the practitioner sees you as perfect as you are and has no investment in changing your attitude, life view, or anything else. You are changing for yourself, not for the practitioner, your spouse, your parents, your children, or your boss.

SESSION COSTS

The more training and experience the practitioner has, the more the session will probably cost. Like a medical doctor or massage therapist, the practitioner has expenses for continuing training, certification, advertising, brochures and cards, website maintenance, office space, cleaning, taxes, professional fees, licenses, insurance, and accounting.

A practitioner who maintains an office will probably charge more than someone who works from home. A practitioner who treats horses where they live may charge for travel time. Practitioners with higher levels of training and certification will charge more than those with less training. Practitioners vary in price per session within the community and across the country. Practitioners who charge more are not necessarily better. Like fine wine, you can find excellent practitioners at affordable prices.

REFERRING YOU TO SOMEONE ELSE

Practitioners refer clients to other energy healers or professionals for a variety of reasons. Perhaps the practitioner isn't neutral about your situation. If the practitioner is your friend and has an investment in the outcome, he/she may not be able to put that aside for treatment. Perhaps the practitioner knows someone more experienced with your particular issue or feels another modality might serve you better. Perhaps the practitioner doesn't feel proficient in the modality you want to receive, even though the practitioner has had some training in it.

If your energy practitioner refers you to a mental health counselor or asks you to get a medical checkup, the practitioner is acting ethically with your best interests in mind. If you need someone to talk with you and help you resolve deep grief, abuse, rejection, unrelenting depression or loss, choose a mental health professional and supplement that treatment with energy therapy. Animal practitioners will ask if you have consulted a veterinarian. If you haven't, they will often recommend doing so. A cat losing weight due to worms probably needs more than an energy session.

The majority of energy clients, both human and animal, also see other health professionals. Western and Eastern medical traditions can complement each other and be complemented by energy work. Kim Martin, DVM and acupuncturist, and I work side by side. Dr. Martin diagnoses, treats, and prescribes; I clear, balance, and support.

NUMBER OF SESSIONS

The number of sessions you need varies with your situation and sometimes with the modality. Reconnective Healing recommends no more than three sessions. You return for additional sessions only if a major event takes place, or six months to a year later.

Chronic issues, such as a disease process leading to death within a few months, benefit from regular sessions to improve comfort and reduce pain. Conditions like arthritis can be positively affected by energy work. Animals that refuse to eat may resume eating after an energy session. Many issues for people and for animals resolve in one session.

Healthy people, including me, schedule energy sessions to maintain our well-being. Energy work maintains our mental, spiritual, emotional, and physical balance. Our healthy animal friends enjoy energy sessions too. They don't need to be ill or traumatized. Give them the gift of an energy session to help them feel great!

INSURANCE COVERAGE

Your health insurance will probably not cover the cost of your energy sessions. However, with increasing demand from consumers, this may change. Insurance companies now pay for massage, acupuncture, and chiropractic treatments. If you have a flexible medical spending account, health care savings account, or similar plan, you may be able to receive reimbursement for energy treatments. Prior to scheduling your session, check with your health plan provider to determine if your expenses will be covered.

Go to practitioners whose scope of practice encompasses your issue. If you want to lose thirty pounds, you might see a medical doctor or naturopath to determine underlying physical issues that might impact your weight. A nutritionist could assist you with healthy food choices. A hypnotherapist can help change your attitudes about eating. A ThetaHealing practitioner can help you clear beliefs that do not serve your highest good about food and your body. All these modalities complement each other. If your Reiki Practitioner advises you on food choices or suggests supplements, it's time to ask whether he/she has training in these areas. Ethical practitioners provide information and advice solely in areas they have studied. Just because your biofield therapist helps you achieve deep relaxation, does not mean he/she is qualified to tell you how to stretch or exercise.

THE RIGHT PRACTITIONER

Sometimes, despite doing research and following the recommendations of others, the practitioner isn't the right one for you. Everything looked right, but the fit between you and the practitioner doesn't feel right. When I needed a chiropractic adjustment for my neck, I asked friends for recommendations. I reviewed websites. I chose a doctor who included the word "intuitive" in the description of her style and services. I wanted to work with her because I assumed she combined intuitive knowledge of the body with her medical knowledge.

When I arrived for my appointment, I noticed her office had a full line of supplements available for purchase. I filled out an extensive medical questionnaire that included information about allergies and other aspects of my health. When we met, she reviewed the questionnaire and asked me detailed questions about my overall well-being. I answered her questions, but explained I was only interested in having my neck adjusted. She talked about the importance of total health. I told her, "If you'll just touch my neck, you'll understand the problem!"

She appeared well versed in the use of supplements to address body issues, but that wasn't why I made an appointment with her. My neck hurt! I wanted an adjustment, not a life change. I left the consultation without having a treatment. I rescheduled with a traditional chiropractor, who provided the relief I sought in one session.

You are in charge. If the practitioner does not listen to you and respond to the level of treatment you want, walk away. Similarly, one treatment is not a commitment to a series of treatments. You do not need to give practitioners a reason for deciding not to return for additional treatments. Your gut feeling is enough.

You may see different energy workers for different issues in your life. Your regular doctor may be a general practitioner.

This does not preclude you from seeing an internal medicine physician. When you schedule energy work for self-care, a safe, comforting, environment where you can release your tension and worries for an hour is enough. Another time, you may be at a transition point in your life and want a series of sessions that support you in taking the next step. If you, your loved one, or your companion animal receives a life-changing diagnosis or is having difficulty with the side effects of cancer treatment, you may prefer a practitioner with a medical background. One practitioner may provide both, but not always. Choose who and what fits your needs at the time.

Recognize the power of energy healing. Imagine how many processes your body does automatically beneath your level of conscious awareness. Picture the processes each cell does every minute! For this reason, I do not recommend seeing two biofield practitioners at the same time, nor do I recommend daily treatments except in life or death situations. Trust the work. If you have a broken leg, seeing two doctors to set the same bone isn't necessary.

Consider seeing a local practitioner first. The founders of different modalities of biofield therapy often have large reputations built on their healing, teaching, and writing. Appointments with them may be difficult to schedule, expensive and require travel. Nearby practitioners took courses offered by the founder or from teacher's trained by the founder. These practitioners may fill your needs as well as the founder.

Dr. Eric Pearl, Reconnective Healing founder, no longer takes private clients. He feels that if he takes clients, it implies that he thinks the practitioners he trained can't do what he does or do it as well. It is not necessary to travel hundreds of miles or spend thousands of dollars to try biofield healing. Use the resources in your community. Try different modalities to find what suits your unique temperament, body, and style. Does the practitioner's work resonate with you? Does the practitioner resonate with you? You are the expert on yourself.

TRUST YOUR GUT

No matter how highly recommended a practitioner may be, or how many other people had terrific results, trust yourself. If you don't like how the practitioner interacts with you or your animal or how the animal reacts to the practitioner, don't go back. You are in charge. Your responsibility is to keep yourself, your children, and your animals safe. If the person, session, or setting doesn't feel right to you, then it isn't.

Practitioners should never promise a cure or threaten dire consequences if you discontinue treatment. Our job is to work for your highest good, recognizing we don't know what that is, and to be neutral toward the outcome. Whatever happens, happens.

Jon had a difficult time with company organizational changes that he felt made it impossible for him to maintain his integrity and meet the demands of the job. He saw the company changes as less about the organization, than about the profession overall and his fit within it. He decided to leave his job and the career he had trained for and worked in for the last ten years. He sought professional counseling to deal with his frustration and anger with the company and for support during his transition to another occupation. The counselor was competent, compassionate, and understanding, but continued to give him information on job openings in the field he was determined to leave. In doing so, the counselor appeared to support a particular outcome instead of working from a neutral perspective. The practitioner's role is not to solve your dilemma, but to honor you as the expert on yourself, capable of meeting any challenge before you, including finding a different line of work.

FOLLOWING YOUR SESSION

The session is complete. You, your loved one, or your animal has spent an hour with an energy practitioner. Now what? In the days that follow, notice what has changed. Healing can happen in an instant or over time. Healing happens when we aren't noticing. It's more difficult for healing to occur when we're always checking to see if we are the same. Compare it to blood pressure—if it's high and you worry about it and check it repeatedly to see if it has come down, chances are it hasn't and it won't.

Dr. Richard Bartlett, Matrix Energetics founder, asks clients to "notice what's different" in the days and weeks following a session. Too often, people notice what's the same—my leg still hurts, I'm still fatigued, I'm still angry. Instead, notice what's different—I was pain free for an hour today; I slept better last night; I experienced moments of joy. If you persist in noticing what is the same, you re-establish it, reinforce it, and repeat it.

Changes may be subtle; they may develop over time. Your healing may not be what you expected or what you hoped. It may be better. Your friends may notice differences that you don't. Energy sessions not only change your energy, but also the energy around you. Look back three to six months after your sessions and ask if there have been positive changes in your life.

Practitioners work for the greatest good of the client, understanding that they do not know what that is. In some situations, the greatest good is not a physical healing; it might be death. Death can be a healing for a being that is suffering. The practitioner doesn't cause the death; the healing is the release from life.

For Reflection

1. What attributes do you want in a practitioner?

_____

_____

_____

_____

_____

2. How much money are you willing to invest in your or your animal's healing?

_____

_____

_____

_____

3. How will you know the practitioner is the right practitioner?

_____

_____

_____

_____

4. How will you know you received a healing?

_____

_____

_____

_____

Chapter Ten
HEALING OTHERS

Healing energy flows through each of us. When I connect to the earth, center myself in the present moment, and set my intention for the greatest good of the other, healing energy from the universe flows through and around me to boost the others' self-healing. Given the opportunity, this same healing stream flows through you too. Remember kissing your child's skinned knee to make it better? Remember resting your hand on a grieving person's arm without speaking?

Some people come into this world knowing they have the capacity to heal others. For most of us, our ability to tap into this stream lies dormant until called upon. Extreme circumstances open the floodgates, and the energy pours over and through us. For others, the ability to heal opens through training. Janet Mentgen, the founder of Healing Touch, wanted every home to have at least one person trained in energy work so healing and comfort was readily available. In one weekend, I learned the basics of Healing Touch and techniques I could use daily on others and myself. You can do the same. Other energetic modalities also offer weekend trainings that open your ability to heal yourself and others.

ENERGY HEALING CAN BE LEARNED

I highly recommend that you take a class in a modality that appeals to you and tap into the power that already exists within you. Below is a student report after her first workshop in Healing Touch for Animals.

Bob, the bobcat at a wildlife rescue organization where I volunteer, became frantic from the noise of heavy construction equipment working nearby. He ran around his enclosure, leapt at the fence, and then tried to burrow under the structures to hide. He panted with his tongue hanging out, yowled and screamed. I began to use the HTA Bridging technique, standing a few feet away. He stopped crying and rolling about and looked at me, staring as I sent intention and allowed energy to flow to him. To my surprise, he lay still, and began to calm down.

In only a few minutes, he heaved a huge sigh, relaxed, stretched out his neck, and changed position to lie on one side. He stretched out his legs toward me and finally, yawned again and again. He eventually rolled over on his back so I could approach and stroke his tummy. This was amazing, given the situation. Truly, a first! He still heard the construction noise and reacted, but on a much lower level, as if he knew it could not hurt him. He "grumble-talked" to me, telling me all about it, almost a purr at times. This was so exciting.

DO-IT-YOURSELF BENEFITS

Discovering that healing energy flows through you and through everyone else is life changing. You have a gift that has lain dormant all these years. Suddenly, the capacity awakens, and you are doing and experiencing things you never thought possible.

When I first discovered energy therapy, I didn't tell anyone–especially the people I worked with and for. I was sure they would think I'd gone over the deep end and was no longer capable of writing logical, detailed, databased, outcome-driven grant applications. After work hours, I was grateful to be in a healing community where talking about unseen energetic phenomena was common, where the experience of feeling energetic hands or pressure on the body during a treatment was met with delight rather than skepticism, where people believed I could do the work more than I believed it myself.

Being with like-minded people is a gift. Many modalities have study groups and service opportunities where you can practice your new skills. Monthly study and practice groups are a source of healing and renewal. They are a place to ask questions, try new techniques, and hone your skills. Being able to help those who are near and dear to you is a wonderful outcome of taking a class. Entry-level workshops in every modality teach powerful tools you can use to help others. More importantly, you can use these tools to help yourself.

Vibrant health and well-being stem from self-care. As wonderful as it is to get an energy healing, it is even more wonderful to sustain that deep peace and relaxation long after the session is complete. Attention to self-care allows that to happen. Self-help resources fill bookstores and the Internet. The market is flooded with "how to improve your life" books. However, experiential energy classes changed my life the most. I learned techniques to clear and balance myself and open my innate ability to self-heal. Through this work, I transformed.

HEALING OTHERS

Are you searching for energy healing for others, rather than for yourself? People sometimes ask if I will send a healing to a friend or relative without that person knowing about it. Consider whether your desire to "heal" another might be a judgment that the person is not perfect as he/she is. Parents want their children to be different. Children want their parents to be different. Spouses want their partners to be different. Employees want their bosses to be different, and bosses want their employees to be different.

We want others to be healthy and whole. However, to love unconditionally is to accept people as they are, to see them as perfect in this moment, to recognize they are doing their best, just as we are. It is challenging to accept others as they are, especially when, in our opinion, they could feel so much better or are behaving badly. Our option is not to change them, but to change ourselves.

No one has to change, or be pain or problem free, for us. The reverse is also true. We do not have to be different for anyone. Who we are in any given moment is our choice, even in the direst of circumstances. Looking back, we may wish we had done things differently, or tried some other options, but we did the best we could at the time. If we could have done better, we would have.

Most energy modalities maintain that we need a person's permission to give a healing. Mary Ellen Flora explains, "A friend of mine is a determined healer and often becomes invasive with her desire to heal. . . . no one can fix, heal or change someone else. . . .We both have lessons about allowing everyone to heal in his or her unique way instead of the way we wish."

Being unattached to the outcome of energy healing is difficult. We want our friends to feel better; we want them to be pain-free. We want to help others, whether they want our help or not. Dr. Eric Pearl maintains "You can only *offer* a healing; you can't *inflict* a healing."

If, from a place of unconditional love, desiring only the highest good for the person with no investment in a particular outcome, I send a healing to someone without prior permission, that healing flows through the universe to the person. The person either accepts or rejects it. According to Dr. Pearl, accepting the healing is giving permission.

FIXING YOURSELF AND OTHERS

You are not broken. You are perfect as you are. You may have aches or disease you want to heal. You may have attitudes and emotions you want to change. You may have a history you regret, or a life you don't want. All that can be true, but you are still perfect as you are. Abraham (channeled by Esther Hicks) says, "Give yourself a break. Give yourself the benefit of the doubt. . . . Love yourself more. Laugh more. Appreciate more. All is well. You can't get it wrong. You never get it done."

A healer who wants to heal you is not neutral. Abraham tells us if we see a person as in need of a healing, then we are approaching that person from a position of us being uncomfortable with how that person is living life. If we are uncomfortable with what someone else is doing, according to Abraham, we are not aligned with our Source. "No lasting value ever

occurs, for two important reasons: first, you are not in alignment with the Energy of your Source, and so you have no real
value to give; and second, your attention to their need only
amplifies their need."

Being unattached to the outcome is a challenge. As healers,
we want to help people. We want our clients to feel better;
we want them to get the healing they came for, in the form
they want. However healing is not about the practitioner or
what the practitioner wants. The practitioner's job is to accept
people as they are, where they are. We create a safe place for
clients to be open to the universe so they can self-heal to the
degree, depth, and breadth that is perfect for them at that
moment. As a healer, I aspire to work from a place of unconditional love, wanting only the highest good for the person or
animal with no investment in the outcome.

A few animals are in situations where if they do not change,
the consequences will be dire. However, this is seldom the
case. The animal care people I meet are compassionate, loving
individuals exploring every possible option to help their animals successfully adjust to their living situations. Energy work
is powerful, but it is not a switch we can flip to change the
basic nature of an animal.

For their animals, people seek veterinary help, possibly chiropractic or acupuncture intervention, make environmental
changes, and engage professional trainers. For themselves,
they see medical professionals, take classes, become better informed, and talk to counselors. Many events occur simultane-
ously in every person's life at any moment. Any one of these
could be the tipping point for a healing. The last thing people
tried prior to their healing or their animal's healing is often

what they say healed them. If Jerry has been to doctors, energy healers, nutritionists, counselors, and the last thing he tries is acupuncture, and then suddenly regains his zest for life, he will probably credit acupuncture for his healing, even though everything he tried before, and his continuing commitment to healing, contributed to the outcome.

All healing is self-healing. Healing is not something that happens outside of you or to you. It happens within you. Medical doctors, chiropractors, naturopaths, shamans, Reiki Masters, Healing Touch, and other energy medicine practitioners can support your body, mind, emotions, and spirit with pills, potions, bodywork, energetic clearing and balancing, and any number of interventions, but neither the person nor the prescription heals your body. You—your body, mind, emotions, and spirit—use what is provided and what is within yourself to self-heal.

The doctor sets the bone; the body knits it together. In *Quantum Healing*, Deepak Chopra asks, "When your body mends a broken bone, why is that not a miracle? As a healing process, it is certainly complex, far too complex for medicine to duplicate. . . ." We are magnificent manifestations of this universe. We are responsible for our bodies, minds, emotions, and spirit. This is a privilege and honor. Two patients go to a physical therapist that assists them with exercises specifically designed to address their issues. They receive handouts with exercises for them to do daily between visits. One patient does the exercises regularly; the other does not. Which one has the better outcome?

If you are looking for something or someone outside yourself to heal you, you will be disappointed. However, if you are looking for someone who will support your self-healing, you may be surprised. According to Chopra, "The reason why not everyone manages to take the healing process as far as it can go is that we differ drastically in our ability to mobilize it."

Many healing modalities are based on one person finding what worked for him or her and sharing that system with others. Dr. Moshe Feldenkrais (1904-1984) was a physicist with a doctorate in engineering and many patents related to the improvement of sonar. He also participated in, taught, and wrote about judo. A series of knee injuries over time resulted in crippling pain. He was offered surgery with a 50 percent possibility of success and a 50 percent chance of being confined to a wheelchair. He declined the surgery and for the next two years turned his attention to the human body and its mechanics. During that time, he experimented on himself and developed new ways to connect his brain, nervous system, and muscles so he could move pain-free. His research led to the restoration of his ability to walk and the development of the Feldenkrais Method. His method, based on very small movements done slowly, has helped millions of people in their healing.

Vianna Stibal, founder of ThetaHealing, relates her story of bone cancer. Medical professionals advised her to have her right leg amputated to give her a little more time to live. She appealed to God. She wanted to know, why her? Why now? She reports, "In the middle of this plea I heard a voice, loud and clear as if someone was standing right next to me in the room. Vianna, you are here with or without a leg, so deal with it." Stibal began a determined effort to heal herself. She discovered a simple method of healing herself and others by working from the deep relaxation of the Theta state and commanding that healing take place. ThetaHealing is now widely taught throughout the U.S. as well as in other parts of the world.

In 1986, Byron Katie pulled herself out of ten years of addiction, anger, and depression when she realized her problems were the result of believing her thoughts were true. When she believed her nerve-racking thoughts were facts, she suffered. When she questioned them, she gained a new perspective. Katie developed a method of inquiry based on four questions that set people free from their negative thoughts. Katie provides extensive information on her technique, video demonstrations and a directory of practitioners on her website.

Louise Hay, famous for her use of affirmations and founder of the publishing company Hay House, Inc., tells her life story in *You Can Heal Your Life*. As a young girl, she was raped, beaten, and abused. At 16, she gave up her newborn baby for adoption. She went through a series of men who mistreated her. Eventually, she found work as a high-fashion model. She married, then divorced after 14 years. In the Church of Religious Science, Hay became interested in metaphysics and healing, and became a church counselor. She studied Transcendental Meditation.

When Hay learned she had cancer, she turned inward to the source of the disease. "If I had an operation to get rid of the cancer and did not clear the mental pattern that created it, then the doctors would just keep cutting Louise until there was no more Louise left to cut. I didn't like that idea."

Hay began an all-out offensive against the cancer. She saw a foot reflexologist, a nutritionist, a therapist. As she cleared her body and her resentments from childhood, she cleared the cancer. Hay writes, "Now I knew from personal experience that dis-ease can be healed, if we are willing to change the way we think and believe and act." Her first book, *Heal Your Body*, lists the metaphysical causes for physical illness. Today, Hay is an icon in the self-help world. Her company, Hay House, publishes many self-help authors. She continues to write on the importance of positive affirmations and living the life you desire. Her story is a testament to the body's ability to self-heal.

Others' systems may work for you or you may piece together your own combination of Western, Eastern, alternative, and complementary interventions. You may develop a program unique to you that results in your healing. Whether you follow someone else's path or blaze your own trail, your healing is your own. Everything you do contributes to your healing.

Excellent books on self-healing are readily available. Most authors were first healers, then teachers, then wrote about their work. Each person has his or her preferred method of healing. Some authors reference authorities from whom they learned; others do not. No system is the only method that works. Many methods work because our bodies have a built-in, self-healing mechanism.

Choose a method that resonates with your desires right now. You may choose something else later or make an addition to what you choose. It doesn't matter. All healing is self-healing. Teachers and authors provide avenues to access your innate capacity.

HEALED OR CURED OR BOTH?

To be healed is to be at peace with yourself and the universe. To be cured is to be rid of a particular disease or condition. You can be healed and not cured; you can be healed and cured; and you can be cured but not healed.

The great physicist and mathematician Stephen Hawking had a progressive motor neuron (Lou Gehrig's) disease that left him in a wheelchair, almost completely paralyzed, needing others to assist him with his basic needs. A bout of pneumonia resulted in a tracheotomy that left him unable to speak.

Hawking learned to use a communication program and speech synthesizer, which he said allowed him to communicate better than he could before the illness. Hawking married twice and fathered three children. In his video, *Stephen Hawking: Does God Exist?*, Hawking says he is dependent on other people, but in his mind, he is free. Perhaps others would look at Hawking's physical condition and say he was ill. I see him as healed.

SELF-CARE IS IMPORTANT

Energy therapy is for people and animals who feel great, too. People and animals in competitive sports benefit from energy work that increases their calm and focus so they can bring their full vitality to the competition. You don't have to be sick or discouraged or in need to benefit from energy work. An energy treatment increases well-being by providing deep relaxation that supports peace. When your mind is quiet, you can let go of the "shoulds" and "oughts." You can hear your inner knowing and gather strength.

Responsibility for our animals and ourselves is not limited to times of illness. Daily self-care supports you and your animals in living vibrant, fulfilling lives. Caring for yourself and your animals includes nutrition, exercise, play, relaxation, and meaningful work; it also includes joy, gratitude, and desire. Our minds need mental stimulation as well as mental quieting; we need challenging puzzles and successful solutions. We need to recognize spirit as senior in our life; to nurture communication between body, mind and spirit; and to access our knowing of what is true for us. Imbalance occurs if we neglect any of these elements.

We can maintain our cars at their peak performance, or we can ignore them and they will continue to function for an extended period. However, when we neglect our vehicles, wear and tear eventually leads to malfunction. The same is true of us. However, if we turn self-care into one more thing we "have to do," then it is no longer self-care; it is one more burden to shoulder. Self-care is a gift we give ourselves, just as caring for our children and our animals is a gift.

The animals in our lives depend on us to keep them healthy and happy. Do you love the animals that live with you to death with food? Or limit their sensory enjoyment through repetitive experiences—the same exercise, the same ball, the same food year after year? Do your animals have opportunities to explore an enriched environment? Do they have exciting play and satisfying jobs? Is their job a struggle between the two of you or a team project?

Healing is a lifelong process. Each of us is ultimately responsible for our well-being. Support yourself through meditation, sound, sleep, play, journaling, time in natural environments, massage—whatever you need to keep yourself in balance and healthy.

For Reflection

1. Do you know a person or animal who self-healed?

_____

_____

_____

_____

_____

2. Do people who have extensive medical interventions self-heal?

_____

_____

_____

_____

3. Do you know a person or animal who was physically cured, but not healed? Why not?

_____

_____

_____

_____

4. If you or your animal healed emotionally, physically, mentally or spiritually, how would daily life be different?

_____

_____

_____

_____

A Final Note

If you are seeking physical, emotional, mental, or spiritual healing for yourself, others, or your animal friends, energy therapy can support you and those you love in the journey toward optimal wellness. Everything you do toward healing contributes to the outcome. You have many options available—allopathic medicine, alternative treatments, complementary modalities, nutrition and supplement support, exercise for your mind and body, behavioral interventions, and more. Read, learn, make informed choices, and do what works for you.

Both medical professionals and the public recognize that "complementary medicine and energy therapies are here to stay, and that these methods can often help the patient who has not found relief from more orthodox approaches" (Oschman, *Energy Medicine*). Scientific evidence to support the effectiveness of energy medicine is growing. In the meantime, the only result that matters is whether it works for you.

Scientists, experts, physicians, and others now recognize that a biomagnetic field within and around plants, animals and humans exists. Energetic fields existed long before scientists could prove they were there. The same is true of chakras, meridians, germs, viruses, other solar systems, and black holes.

Scientific evidence is useful and valuable, but it is not the determinant of what exists and does not exist.

Our ability to heal ourselves and to heal others is resident within us. We have all observed dogs and cats licking themselves to heal their wounds. When the wound is beyond their ability to heal, we support them with allopathic and/or complementary modalities to self-heal. The doctor may provide the salve, the energy worker may clear and balance the field, but the body's innate intelligence heals the wound.

TRANSFORMING YOUR LIFE

Healing is about choices—choices to treat or not to treat, to choose one type of intervention over another, or to choose one method of treatment in conjunction with another. We have the power to make choices for our dependents, our animals, and ourselves. One choice does not eliminate all other possibilities. You can choose and choose again. The most important choice is the decision to heal; all else follows.

Healing is influenced by the demands in our lives, the support of our loved ones, the peacefulness of our surroundings, our attitude towards healing and curing, our view of life, death, and life after death. If we believe our lives and the lives of our animals extend beyond this realm, death becomes less final and less devastating.

If we believe our lives end with our physical bodies, or that we must conform to a particular life philosophy, then our time living will be consumed by fulfilling the demands of our beliefs and the pressure of only one opportunity to get it right. Death of a loved one may be accompanied by grief and regret that seems irresolvable. If you believe your illness is a punishment for a deed done in this life or a past life, that is the framework from which you will experience your illness.

Healers and doctors do not change your life view. They support you where you are. The questions of life beyond this one and punishments for past deeds are yours to resolve. Having said this, there are energy workers and modalities that address clearing past life issues. If you believe past deeds are the reason for your health issues, seek a healer with this expertise.

Remember, you can do this too. Training and experience help you access your innate abilities. The more training you acquire, the more experiences you have healing yourself and others, and the more time you spend self-healing, the more proficient you become. If you need a small repair for your car, you might ask a neighbor who is handy with cars to help you out. If you have a bigger issue, you might go to a friend who moonlights doing repairs. However, if your car needs a major repair, you would choose a qualified professional. The same is true of energy workers. Choose one who fits you and your situation.

NOW WHAT?

You have learned about energy therapy options, the evidence for its efficacy, the concept of healing on multiple levels, energy healing for animals, and distance healing. You have guidelines for choosing a practitioner. You know the difference between healing and curing, and understand the concept of healing into death.

It is time to take action. Begin the process.

Move beyond your comfort zone. If what you've been doing isn't working, do something different. If you are healthy, happy, and look forward to every day, but are curious about energy therapy, schedule an appointment. Life could be even better.

- Choose a modality that appeals to you.

- Locate a practitioner through the modality's website; get referrals from other healing professionals and friends.

- Schedule a consultation. Get your questions answered. Be aware that practitioners of a particular modality will vary. Some will offer the modality exactly as described; some will include other modalities in the treatment; some may be clairvoyant and include their perceptions with the treatment. Practitioners may do more than indicated in practitioner directories or on their websites.

- Trust your gut. Do you resonate with the practitioner? Do you have confidence in the person?

- Experience a session.

- Observe what's different in the days and week afterwards.

Want to be an energy healing practitioner? You can. The capacity to heal others and ourselves resides within each of us. Open yourself to the potential within you.

- Read the information on the modality website.

- Read the founder's book.

- Talk to the coordinator of classes in your area.

- Talk to the instructor.

- Take the introductory course.

- Offer sessions to family and friends.

- What is their experience? What is your experience as a practitioner?

You have the opportunity to heal yourself and others. Take action. Schedule an appointment. Register for a class. Expand what is possible in your life.

I would love to hear from you. Where are you in your journey? Was something in this book especially meaningful to you? Is there information you want that isn't included? Do you have a healing story you'd like to share? Do you have unanswered questions? Email me at Wanda@WandaBuckner.com or visit my website and schedule a complimentary consultation.

We are all in process. We are never done. We are doing the best we can. Our lives are healing journeys. We help each other on the way, whether we know it or not.

I wish you well, now and always. Your friend,

Wanda Buckner

Resources and Recommended Reading

Arom, K. and Barbara MacIntyre. "The Efficacy of Healing Touch in Coronary Artery Bypass Surgery." *Alternative Therapies in Health and Medicine*, July-August 2008.

> This article details the results of a randomized study of the effects of Healing Touch on 237 patients following coronary artery bypass surgery.

Bartlett, Richard. *Matrix Energetics: the Science and Art of Transformation*. Atria Books. NY. 2007.

> Bartlett bases his work on the concept of infinite possibilities. He teaches the use of past, future and parallel realities as healing possibilities—bringing a preferred situation from another time or place into the present. Matrix Energetics includes many additional techniques.

Bryne, Rhonda. *The Secret*. Atria Books. NY. 2006.

> The film and book of the same name are based on the philosophy that we can attract into our lives those things we desire by focusing on what is going right and where we want to go rather than dwelling on what we lack.

Carlson, Richard, and Shield, Benjamin, eds. *Healers on Healing.* G.P. Putnam's Sons. NY. 1989.

> This book is a compilation of short essays by the major names in energy healing in the 1980's including Bernie Siegel. The essays are grouped into topics: Love is the Healer, Returning to Wholeness, The Healer Within, The Healing Relationship, The Role of the Healer, The Healing Attitude, Consciousness and the Healing Response, and Healing is Our Birthright. If you are interested in the foundational thoughts that shaped energy healing, you will enjoy this book.

Center for Reiki Research. http://www.centerforreikiresearch.org/.

> This excellent site provides summaries of published, peer reviewed, evidence based research on the efficacy of Reiki. A list of hospitals, medical clinics and hospice programs that use Reiki is included. Access to the site materials is through a free membership.

Chopra, Deepak. *Quantum Healing: Exploring the Frontiers of Mind/Body Medicine.* Bantam Books. NY. 1989.

> Reading this book will expand your wonder at the capacities of our bodies, and increase your belief in the body's ability to self-heal. Chopra's and others' experiences with miraculous healings led him to believe in the mind's ability to change the body's response to disease. He says, "Quantum healing is the ability of one mode of consciousness (the mind) to spontaneously correct the mistakes of another mode of consciousness (the body)." He postulates that a powerful, unseen force exists that continually influ-

ences our beings. "The material body is a river of atoms, the mind is a river of thought, and what holds them together is a river of intelligence."

Co, Master, and Robins, Eric. *Your Hands Can Heal You: Pranic Healing Energy Remedies to Boost Vitality and Speed Recovery from Common Health Problems.* Free Press. 2002.

Part I, "How Your Body and Mind Work" discusses the energetic body and the mind. Part II, "The Six Steps to Self-Healing" covers "Clearing Negative Emotions and Limiting Beliefs, Pranic Breathing, Energy Manipulation, Energetic Hygiene, Meditation, and Energy Generation Exercises." Parts III and IV focus on "Staying Energized and Healthy" and "Beyond Physical Health." This book is a how-to manual that includes a daily energetic, self-healing routine. The introduction to the book includes self-reports of people who successfully used the methods described to relieve a severe burn, heal a cerebral aneurysm, and heal a deep puncture wound.

Flora, Mary Ellen. "A Spiritual Perspective." November 2012. www.c-d-m.org.

Mary Ellen Flora is a clairvoyant reader, spiritual teacher and healer. She writes on healing, meditation and spirituality. Her eBooks are available at Smashwords.com and Espirit.com.

Fundamentals of Complementary and Alternative Medicine. Edited by Marc S. Micozzi. 4th Edition. Saunders. 2011.

This comprehensive, scholarly text is written by experts and peer reviewed. The in-depth articles are well researched and thought provoking. Sidebars provide additional information that supplements the main text. The book is divided into six sections: Foundations of Complementary and Alternative Medicine, Mind, Body, and Spirit (includes electricity, light and magnetism), Manual Therapies (such as massage and touch therapies), Alternative Western Therapies (examples are naturopathic, herbalism, aromatherapy), Traditional Ethnomedical Systems: Asia (includes acupuncture, Qi Gong and Ayurveda), Traditional Ethnomedical Systems: Africa and the Americas (includes Native American healing, South American spiritism and Latin American Curanderismo). Intended for the serious student, the book's scope is broader and deeper than most works in this field. A companion website provides additional resources.

Grandin, Temple, with Johnson, Catherine. *Animals in Translation: Using the Mysteries of Autism to Decode Animal Behavior.* Scribner. NY. 2005.

Grandin uses her experience of being autistic and thinking differently than non-autistic people to reflect on how animals may think and perceive the world. Her insights into animals' highly specific responses to their world and lack of generalizing from one situation to another helps us understand why seeing a man with a hat in the barn is not the same as seeing a man in a hat in the field. This is only one of the many useful and interesting insights she provides.

Hay, Louise. *You Can Heal Your Life.* Hay House, Inc. 1984.

Hay's personal story of tragedy and recovery from cancer are the background for her discovery that positive affirmations can bring what is desired into reality. Available in many formats, this handbook has been in use for decades.

Healing Touch for Animals. HealingTouchforAnimals.com.

This site provides information on the modality, its founder Carol Komitor, courses offered, how Healing Touch works, and a practitioner directory. Brief information on using essential oils with animals is also included.

Healing Touch Program. HealingTouchProgram.com.

This site provides information on Healing Touch, courses offered, resources related to Healing Touch and a practitioner directory.

Healing Touch Research Survey. Healing Touch International. Updated annually.

This booklet summarizes all current research on Healing Touch from cancer to work stress. Available at HealingTouchInternational.org

Herzog, Nat. *Some We Love, Some We Hate, Some We Eat: Why It's So Hard to Think Straight About Animals.* HarperCollins Publishers. NY. 2010.

Herzog observes and comments on our behaviors and attitudes toward animals from an anthrozoology viewpoint. This highly readable book will challenge your beliefs about our relationships with animals.

Hicks, Esther and Jerry. *Getting into the Vortex Guided Meditation CD and User Guide.* Hay House, Inc. 2010.

Esther Hicks channels Abraham, a group of non-physical beings, who teach that the Law of Attraction brings about our experiences. By thinking of what we desire, we bring it into existence. The book and CD set has four sections with meditations on General Well-Being, Financial Abundance, Physical Well-Being, and Relationships. The meditations and text increase positive thoughts and release resistance to well-being.

Hover-Kramer, Dorothea. *Healing Touch Guidebook: Practicing the Art and Science of Human Caring.* Healing Touch Program. San Antonio, Texas. 2009.

Hover-Kramer was active in Healing Touch with Janet Mentgen, the founder, from the beginning days. Section I provides a "Framework for Understanding the Practice of Healing Touch" including the "History and Theories of Energy Healing" and "The Research Basis of Healing Touch." Section II describes "Healing Touch Practices and Coursework." Section III discusses Healing Touch in health care settings. The last section is devoted to the "Ongoing Development of the Healing Touch Practitioner." The Code of Ethics in the Appendices states the practitioner standards.

Jain, Shamini and Paul J. Mills. "Biofield Therapies: Helpful or Full of Hype? A Best Evidence Synthesis." *International Journal of Behavioral Medicine.* 2009. 17:1-16.

This article is often cited in reference to the value of energy work. The authors analyzed and summarized the results of 66 research studies. The journal publishes original research articles as well as integrative reviews on heath and illness.

Judith, Anodea. *Wheels of Life: A User's Guide to the Chakra System.* 2nd Ed. Llewellyn Publications. St. Paul, MN. 2000.

Judith introduces the concept of chakras, then provides in-depth information on each of the seven major chakras followed by more general chapters. Glossary, bibliography and index included. If you are deeply interested in the role of chakras, you will enjoy this book.

Krieger, Delores. *The Therapeutic Touch: How to Use Your Hands to Help or to Heal.* Prentice Hall Press. 1979.

Krieger discusses our natural healing potential and outlines the basics of hands on healing: the healer goes to a place of inner stability; uses his/her hands to assess the bio-field; moves energy within the field to increase the natural flow; then uses "conscious direction" to help the client self-heal. Krieger writes about how we can help others heal and discusses her experiences as a researcher and healer.

Morris, Joyce. *Reiki: Hands That Heal.* Red Wheel/Weiser LLC. York Beach, ME. 1999.

Morris' book can be used as a text for teaching or learning Reiki. She covers the history of Reiki, the Reiki principles, ethics, legal considerations, the three degrees and hand positions. Newer information on Reiki research is available on the Internet.

Murray, Ken. "How Doctors Die: It's Not Like the Rest of Us, But It Should Be."
zocalopublicsquare.org/2011/11/30/how-doctors-die/ideas/nexus/

Murray says doctors don't die like the rest of us; they die with much less intervention when faced with life-ending conditions. He describes doctors' frustration with "futile care" that increases the quantity of a person's life by a small amount, but decreases the quality of life immensely.

National Center for Complementary and Alternative Medicine (NCCAM). National Institutes of Health. United States Department of Health and Human Services. nccam.nih.gov/

NCCAM is the "lead agency for scientific research on the diverse medical and health care systems, practices, and products that are not generally considered part of conventional medicine." Their mission is to research the usefulness and safety of CAM practices in improving health. This is an authoritative source on the researched outcomes of many complementary modalities.

Oschmann, James L. *Energy Medicine: The Scientific Basis.* Elsevier Ltd Churchill Livingston. 2000.

Oschmann explains how energy medicine is currently in use by the medical community for diagnosis and treatment. He discusses the measurable energy frequencies used for healing and the energy, such as in acupuncture, that we cannot yet measure, but can see the results. This is an excellent technical resource on the science behind energy medicine.

Pearl, Eric. *The Reconnection: Heal Others, Heal Yourself.* Hay House. Carlsbad CA. 2001.

Pearl tells his compelling story of changing careers from a chiropractor in Hollywood to a healer interacting with a new frequency of light, information, and energy. Part I is about "The Gift." Part II covers "Reconnective Healing and What it Means." Part III is "You and Reconnective Healing." This book will not tell you how to do Reconnective Healing, but it will tell you how Reconnective Healing came unsought and unexpectedly to Pearl and the philosophy behind the modality.

Reconnective Healing. TheReconnection.com.

The official site of Reconnective Healing provides information on this energy modality, the schedule of classes, testimonials and related topics.

Schoen, Allen M. & Proctor, Pam. *Love, Miracles, and Animal Healing: A Heartwarming Look at the Spiritual Bond between Animals and Humans.* New York, NY: Fireside, 1996.

Schoen writes of his personal experiences from deciding to become a veterinarian, through the rigors and scientific approach of Cornell School of Veterinary Medicine to his exploration of complementary modalities to support animals' healing, including the use of loving touch, acupuncture, Chinese herbs, and homeopathy. The book concludes with a chapter on how animals have been, and continue to be, his teachers.

Schwartz, Gary E., PhD with Simon, William L. *The Energy Healing Experiments: Science Reveals our Natural Power to Heal.* Atria Books. New York, NY. 2007.

If you are interested in the science behind energy healing, read this book. Schwartz speaks to the physics of energy, laboratory experiments, and implications for the future.

His premises are expressed in the book sections: Part I Everything has Energy and Conscious Intention; Part II Our Energy Fields Connect Us with Everything; Part III All Healing Involves Energy and Conscious Intention.

Stibal, Vianna. *ThetaHealing: Go Up and Seek God; Go Up and Work with God.* Rolling Thunder Publishing. Idaho Falls, ID. 2006.

Stibal tells her personal story of self-healing. She believes a belief in a "Creator of All That Is," by whatever name we use, is central to healing oneself and others. Stibal teaches students to reach a Theta state from where healing is done by a command to the Creator of All That Is.

Thomas, Linnie. *The Encyclopedia of Energy Medicine.* Fairview Press. Minneapolis, MN. 2010.

Thomas summarizes 17 Eastern Energy Modalities and 15 Western Modalities. She provides a brief history of each one followed by course descriptions and other information such as resources and suggested reading. This is a good resource for short descriptions and training information on a variety of modalities.

Wagner, Sarah. "It's All About Energy." *Animal Wellness Magazine.* Redstone Media Group. Vol. 15, Issue 3.

Wagner discusses what energy medicine is and why it works. *Animal Wellness* covers topics of interest to people with dog or cat companion animals.

Zemach-Bersin, David and Kaethe, and Reese, Mark. *Relaxercise: the Easy New Way to Health & Fitness.* Harper. San Francisco. 1990.

Though not a book on energy healing, the exercises provided can make a difference in your life. The exercises are based on Dr. Moshe Feldenkrais' method of small movements done slowly. A few minutes a day doing targeted exercises from this book relieves pain and tension, and increases flexibility and ease.

About the Author

Wanda is an author, healer, teacher, speaker, life coach, clairvoyant, and animal communicator. When she discovered she had healing hands, she left a traditional career in education and proposal writing to one dedicated to healing herself and others.

Wanda maintains an active practice supporting the mental, emotional, physical and spiritual healing of people and animals. Sessions are at her office in Olympia WA, through distance healing, or house calls. Wanda offers classes and coaching in person, by phone and over the Internet. Coaching clients choose from a menu of individualized services that includes self-exploration and self-directed change with energetic support. Wanda speaks on the use of energy therapy to transform the lives of people and animals.

Wanda is a certified Healing Touch Program (for people) and Healing Touch for Animals Practitioner, a Reiki Master, and an Infinite Possibilities Certified Trainer. She brings her experience, knowledge, intuition, and extrasensory perception to every session.

For more information or to schedule a complimentary consultation, go to www.WandaBuckner.com.